THE CHINA CARD

THE CHINA CARD

A NOVEL BY

DONALD FREED

ARBOR HOUSE
New York

ACKNOWLEDGMENTS

For helping me imagine one version of 1984 I am indebted to a number of scholars and researchers: Franz Schurmann, Sandy Close and Pacific News Service, Irving Sarnoff and the Alliance for Survival, Victor Marchetti, Peter Dale Scott, Fred S. Landis, Robert C. Cohen, that superb critic Halina Charwat, Harold Lieberman, James Cookson and Kirk Vinson and the Citizens Research and Investigating Committee, and Jackie Stehr. And then there is my companion and editor P.R.F., who gave me the key.

For M and K and H—with love.

"Man is the product of causes which had no prevision of the end they were achieving . . . no fire, no heroism, no intensity of thought and feeling, can preserve an individual life beyond the grave . . . yet despite ultimate extinction we must live constantly in the vision of the good . . ."

Lord Bertrand Russell

THE CHINA CARD

January 12, 1984

SENATE COMMITTEE CHALLENGES ADMINISTRATION
SENATOR DELLUMS CHARGES
SECRET U.S.-CHINA NUCLEAR DEAL

BY

BETSY JONES-RUSSELL

(SPECIAL CORRESPONDENT TO THE LONDON TIMES)

WASHINGTON—Amidst an aura of alarm not felt in this capital since the Cuban missile crisis, the United States Senate acted today to exercise its constitutional rights concerning the power to make war.

The Foreign Relations Committee of the Senate demanded that Wolfgang H. Manheim, the President's powerful adviser on National Security Affairs, appear before the prestigious Senate unit in executive session. Senator Glenn Bower (R-Tex.), speaking for the minority members, stated that, "There is the smell of Pearl Harbor in the air," referring to the Japanese attack on the naval base in World War II.

In a related development Senator R. K. Dellums (D-Cal.) announced today that he would "go to the country" to tell the public the truth about "the impending and terrifying possibility of thermonuclear war breaking out between the United States and China on the one side and the Soviet Union on the other." Senator Dellums stated that he "had evidence" but "not proof" that the U.S. and China had reached "a secret and unconstitutional agreement" concerning the use of nuclear weapons against the USSR.

(Please turn to page 13, column 2)

1

1

WASHINGTON, D.C.—JANUARY 13, 1984 (FRIDAY)

BETSY JONES-RUSSELL: Tape one, side one . . . testing, testing . . . January 13, the year of our Lord 1984. At the Watergate Apartments, first interview with the Honorable W. H. Manheim. Dr. Manheim, there is a wire service story that the center ruling party of Japan may be brought down over its support for the U.S. policy of Japanese rearmament, which critics are calling the *real* China Card, and—these goddamn helicopters are impossible. They *are* spying on us, aren't they? Really, Dr. Manheim, as National Security Adviser, couldn't you call the White House about these dreadful green machines? I think . . .

She depressed the REWIND button. The big khaki-colored military helicopter hovered in a holding position outside the double windows while a Secret Service agent, inside, pressed a walkie-talkie against his mouth. The concussion from the rotors shook the entire suite. Inside her head, to herself, she shouted over the terrific chopping sound—"Watch out, don't fly into a rage—this mother ain't no piece of cake like little Henry Kissinger"—in what she fancied was an American dialect.

Four aides stood behind his chair, hanging over the high-muscled shoulders of the President of the United States's National Security Adviser. Each held out a memo for the man to speed-read. From the kitchen, she thought she heard the sound of Secret Service agents breaking dishes or something. The helicopter had started to withdraw, but it was still impossible to talk, so she gave her nervous gaze rein to rove about the "power environment"—she would need a more exact phrase—and to make mental notes while Manheim gave his attention to the memos.

The suite was unlike any other, she was sure, in the entire Watergate Complex. More than six hundred square feet, she guessed, besides the small kitchen and the den or bedroom off of the foyer. No, he couldn't actually live in this laboratory setting, where wide windows seemed to have been designed to allow the surcharged official helicopters constant visual access to the meetings and machinations taking place here. Some GSA designer had captured the big square main room in gray and blue, she decided, so that the inhabitants would be like insects set in wax in a K Box—open at one end so that the flying metallic organisms could scrutinize them at will.

She studied the heads bobbing around the long, almost tragic mask of a face of W.H. (Wolfgang Helmut) Manheim. She was accustomed to earning the enmity of the palace guard of whichever great man she happened to be bearding for one of her celebrated London *Times* "portraits," but this Manheim National Security staff was particularly grim, worse than the Kissinger groupies (how he had hated that phrase). No, this little cabal, she decided, would be dubbed "a gang of 1984 *epigoni.*"

She watched Manheim's lucid and intelligent face frown and focus on memo after memo in almost lightning succession. This is a man, she told herself, who might appreciate the word *"epigoni"* and some of the other arcane vocabulary she liked to use in her prize-winning portraits of the great of the world.

The helicopter began its final pivot out of the Watergate Complex so she took the plunge and punched the ON button.

BETSY JONES-RUSSELL: . . . I think a bit louder . . . Uh, Dr. Manheim, the ground rules we discussed are, I believe, a series of, let's say, half a dozen short interviews—no photographs—and a copy of all tapes to your office within one week of completion. I believe that Mr. Kott has all this plus—

WOLFGANG MANHEIM: Plus the actual manuscript and the *original* of the tapes.

B. J-R: I'm not quite clear on why fair copies of the tapes won't do.

W.M.: You, the great girl reporter, you ask this question about interviews taking place in the Watergate?

B. J-R: Ah, I think I see what you mean . . . "Girl Reporter" I'll let pass. Now, perhaps we should—

W.M.: I hope the presence of the Secret Service people won't bother you. Let's see, you have met Peter Wick, my assistant, who will be keeping track of the time for us. And Andy Kott, and his aides Katy Brown and Ray Anderson, and then there are *their* aides—

B. J-R: But we're almost out of time already. Ah, Mr. Wick, you will, I take it, deduct any telephone call interruptions from the allotted time? Right. Well, sir, since that day when Mr. Nixon described the United States as a "pitiful giant," your country has suffered the most serious losses in southern and western Africa, at least three humiliations in Iran, reverses across the Middle East—

"Dr. Manheim, the President is on the line."

She watched him rise and stride, the aides scrabbling in his wake, toward the study or situation room or whatever it was. She dug in her tote bag for some notes, and as she looked up she caught one of the Secret Service men staring at her. She glared him down and back into the kitchen. "Horny young Arrow collar killer type," she thought, knowing how she looked in the tailored Ann Klein suit and shirt; how the gray weave set off her steel-blue eyes and honey hair caught in a chignon . . .

She stood and stretched, smiling as she read, upside down, several exposed clips from the official folder nearest to her on the large glass coffee table.

January 12, 1984

U.S., CHINA ASSAIL VIETNAM
FOR THAILAND BORDER ATTACK
BEIJING WARNS OF
THREAT TO REGION

BEIJING—China condemned the Vietnamese invasion of Thailand and apparently put its troops along the Sino-Vietnamese border on alert Wednesday, a sign that Beijing may be preparing to go to the aid of the Thais.

Diplomatic and military sources here predict massive Chinese retaliation against Soviet-sponsored Vietnam, for they
Please turn to page 8, column 1

MANHEIM REAFFIRMS
PLEDGE TO BANGKOK
BY
BETSY JONES-RUSSELL

WASHINGTON—National Security Adviser Wolf Manheim on Wednesday condemned Vietnamese military attacks across the Cambodian border into Thailand and called on the Soviet Union to restrain its Vietnamese ally.

Manheim's statement pledged that the United States will "stand by its commitments" to Thailand under a 1954 agreement that has been periodically reaffirmed.

That agreement provides that in case of "aggression by armed attack," which endangers peace and security, "each party will act to meet the common danger in accordance with its constitutional processes."

Meanwhile, it was disclosed that the United States will sell Thailand 35 M-48 tanks and associated equipment, worth $23 million. The sale was re-

Please turn to page 9, column 1

MANHEIM PROFILE—B. J. RUSSELL
continued from page 3

A specialist in Soviet-American affairs, Manheim urges us to reflect carefully on the unimaginable destructiveness of military, political and economic forces building up around the world. These forces, he submits, are too much like those that created Auschwitz; for example, a combination of high technology and low regard for human life was necessary to unleash the Holocaust. Today's nuclear arms race involves those factors, too. Weakness only tempts aggressors, and thus Manheim finds no remedy in unilateral disarmament. Instad, he bets on "the expansion of economic ties and human contacts between East and West" as an indispensable first step toward world peace.

In 1945, the President's chief adviser was liberated by a black American soldier. Now his vision of blood and hope prods the United States to do its part to rescue the world. Success in that task depends, Manheim says, on the same traits that helped him to live through the Holocaust: clarity of mind; capacity to endure and to invent; conviction that "the struggle for survival in freedom must begin with oneself."

Who is Wolf Manheim?

"Who's Wolf Manheim, indeed," she repeated to herself. She looked up and away as the other Secret Service man crossed the room toward the bathroom.

"There will be no fraternizing with the bodyguards," she commanded herself, recalling an episode in Uganda, then she began to muse about Andrew Kott, the one of all the aides she would call human. He was the overweight, balding, nail-biting whiz kid in his early thirties who represented the "left wing" of the National Security Adviser's staff (and that was a stretch, since Dr. Kott was a Polish Kremlinologist particularly despised by the Soviets). Yet Andy, as she decided she would call him, did throw off the ineluctable scent of a young man with a formidable brain, "and no woman can completely resist that organ," she soliloquized, drumming her slim, unringed hands on her flat belly as she leaned back into the couch, waiting. Then there was Peter Wick. "Danger," she thought, and passed to Ms. Brown, who was black and striking. "Which one or ones is she sleeping with?" Musing, "Certainly the great man, and possibly the runt, Andy Kott." No, Kott wore a wedding ring—if that meant anything. The other aide, Anderson, didn't count, "California type," she yawned out loud and flopped her long body on the divan again as the man of the hour reentered with his staff, laughing. *Newspapers speculating about World War III and they're laughing. I suppose that's good,* she thought. Out loud, she merely cleared her throat and jabbed at the RECORD button again.

> B.J-R.: You said, Dr. Manheim—Wolf—Oh, does smoking bother you?
>
> W.M.: No, but it drives the SS boys, the Secret Service, into a panic. . . . No, go ahead, maybe they'll leave us alone.
>
> B.J-R.: No, I'm trying to stop. Do you actually call the Secret Service "SS"?—You do? Well, that's good to know . . . Ah, you said that you're not certain whether we can meet again tomorrow, or Sunday. This is no problem for me. I'm staying next door at the Watergate Hotel, and I'll just stand by until I hear from you. I know that with what's happening you'll be pressed—

W.M.: I'm pressed for time, yes. The President wants me to leave for China within the week.

B.J-R.: Yes, of course. Can you respond to European press charges that China and the U.S.—I'm referring to your upcoming Beijing trip—are drawing up contingency war plans? . . . I beg your pardon? Umm, you are *not* responding to that charge? . . . Well, then let me erase this small talk and we can get started . . .

Peter Wick emerged from the other room to signal that someone of importance wanted to speak to the National Security Adviser. Manheim rose with a sigh and stalked out. In the charcoal Brooks Brothers suit he appeared even taller and leaner than his photograph. Everything about him looked to her to be lean, abstracted, as if he were come to life from a fifteenth-century German woodcut. A medieval knight, she decided, that was what he put her in mind of. His eyes were deep, dark—"haunted," she would later write, his shoulders hunched as if the hand of the God of the Middle Ages were gripping them. The bony face was pale and hard, and, to her, compelling, almost beautiful in a distinctly unmodern way. His hair was light brown and fine, cropped close to the long elegant skull. She kept trying to recall whom he reminded her of.

Peter Wick interrupted her fugue by bumping the table as he passed on his way to the kitchen, so she turned her much written about critical faculty on the lean and hungry Dr. Wick. "All Poles and no Jews," her smoky eyes narrowed, "or maybe Andy Kott was, half." Hmm, that might explain the minor interest that his skinny, poorly tailored figure had caused her. "Stop identifying with the victim," she lectured herself, breaking a cigarette in half, "there's a world crisis unfolding and there won't be time for sex this trip, much less with the entire staff . . . think about something else, something *not* sexual—like Peter Wick's green skin.

Wick and Kott were Poles left over from Zbig Brzezinski's shock troops. Why were they now attached to the most celebrated American dove since Adlai Stevenson? Wolf Manheim—the "civilized soldier," *Time* had called him in the "Man of the Year" cover story. American politics had become, since Vietnam, "like the House of Atreus," she had written in the introduction to her verbal portrait of Henry Kissinger. Kissinger had gone down, and the dove Vance had risen, only to be torn apart by the hawk Brzezinski. Then, the Ayatollah and Billy Carter, between them, had destroyed Zbig, and Wolf Manheim had risen from the ashes. Now both the Chinese and the Soviets were insisting on negotiating only with Manheim, and the hawkish Secretary of State, Clare Higgins III, was letting it leak that he would quit as soon as the crisis had peaked. With Higgins would go the ultra-Right—leashed in for four long years, starting to call hoarsely for Manheim's blood . . .

She knew that the dangerous contradiction all across the American power circle was fueled by much more than thunder on the Right. Since the days of Dean Rusk and Walt Whitman Rostow, the balance of diplomatic power had shifted away from the State Department to the National Security Council. A strong president could manipulate and play off State and the NSC against the Pentagon, or against each other. But there had not been a strong president since . . . "And they killed him," she reflected, staring without looking through the wall of windows, waiting for the helicopter to return.

Higgins's appointment had been a political payoff and Manheim had been ordered into the cabinet by the "Bank," as the Establishment was referred to in the 1983 Betsy Jones-Russell/Gore Vidal correspondence featured in *Esquire*. The great center forces of American capital, the Rockefeller circle, had always feared the Right more than the Left—". . . and what does that say about your liberals and your Left?" she had written, questioning Vidal.

Now, as she broke another cigarette in half and stared out over the stone Watergate vista, she realized how prophetic her published exchange with Vidal had been. For that matter, power had been an out of control centrifuge in America for many years. What did anyone expect?

There would, she knew, never be another John Foster Dulles. The Department of State, "Foggy Bottom," was a huge, elite bureaucracy, full of leaks. Compared to this many-thousand-headed monster, Wolf Manheim's NSC was a tight and effective human computer with a staff of less than fifty.

Before the crisis, even a weak chief executive had sometimes been able to protect his wavering standing in the polls by pitting his hawk, Higgins, against his dove, Manheim. Except that Manheim was the hawk—or a condor or an eagle, in terms of attack and tactics, in terms of power politics—and the "Bank" knew that; and not only Wall Street but Fleet Street, NATO and the rest of the West knew it too.

Behind the scenes, and through a series of leaks to his "elite assets" in the news media, Manheim had ridiculed the hard-line campaign to send a task force to the Ogaden region of Ethiopia to confront Soviet- and Cuban-backed forces. Manheim was reported to have stood to his full height and announced to the suddenly awake President, during a showdown in the Oval Office, "Mr. President, Defense and State can never get it right, for some reason. The *Somalis* are the aggressors, they *started it!*"... Wolf Manheim had won that argument, as well as the one about censuring the U.S. allies following their rapid acquisition of nuclear weapons.

So it, the secret war behind the scenes, had gone on for four years, while the public was almost completely obsessed with the economic disaster that was now reaching into every home in the country. Manheim was a mystery to the public; with inflation increasing dramatically since 1980 and Chrysler and Ford depressed, only the "Bank" really knew what a tall figure of authority Manheim was in a White House close to panic over the upcoming elections.

"Manheim," Betsy Jones-Russell had concluded to Gore Vidal,

"is the man to watch in 1984. If he is unable to bring off the hat trick"—(1) face down the Bad Old Boys at State and CIA, (2) psychoanalyze the Chinese, and (3) put the fear of history into the Russians—"then George Orwell's *1984* image of all against all in the name of 'Security and Freedom' will have left the drawing board. The rough beast of the future will be reported as having been sighted in the suburbs, its hour come round at last."

Still, she pondered, if Manheim was in control and closest to the President, why the presence of the kid Kott and skinny Dr. Wick? These two men were Polish Catholic aristocrats like Brzezinski. They hated Russians—not communism, but *Russians.* And they disdained Americans. Americans were lazy, stupid and corrupt to the foreign-born elite of the U.S. diplomatic and National Security establishment. Manheim was not that type at all—was he? After all, he was a Jewish survivor of Buchenwald, very different, indeed. And he certainly didn't despise women the way the anteater Wick did. Hamlet, she thought, fallen among thieves . . . . Wick dogtrotted across the room toward the kitchen. Were those *red* socks? A secret solipsist into the bargain. "Guildenstern," she thought.

Peter Jan Wick: predatory, hyperthyroid . . . why did she hate him so on sight? Because she knew the type, male and female. The ones who follow great ones. The psychoanalyst in London had explained it to her once, what was that catchy phrase again? Oh, yes, "The shadow of the object falls across the ego." And when Norman had attacked her and called her "the great man's moll," he had had, as usual, a kernel, a seedling of truth.

Under cover of offering her tea, the younger Secret Service agent was measuring her silk-shirt-sheathed breasts. The standard-issue reflecting sunglasses were supposed to hide the eyes, but she pretty well knew his type too. Though maybe it wasn't even her nipples, perhaps he was actually grasping, in his mind's eye, at her mound of Venus, where he imagined it lay in wait for him under her loosely pleated tweed trousers.

"How nice. Just a bit of milk, please." He moved away, like a cat in a Hickey-Freeman blue suit, toward the half-kitchen. She stacked her notes impatiently against the glass tabletop. "Jesus, just let me get out of this town," she said to herself. She had been waiting in Washington since before Christmas for Wolfgang "Wolf" Manheim, to find eight hours for the long-awaited London *Times* interviews. "What's this?"

"Milk."

"Milk?"

"You said—"

"Milk! Tea with *milk*. As in tea with *lemon* or coffee with . . . ."

She remembered that they were called SS for short as he wheeled and quickstepped back to the kitchen. She looked toward the closed door. Four-thirty already. Again she wondered if it was possible that Wolf Manheim, the power diplomat, actually *lived* in the Watergate? No, she decided, it was not possible. This—what would she call it in her atmosphere sidebar accompanying the interview? —this "early Watergate," the word was already generic.

"Here you are."

Before she could find just the right words to thank the all-American agent with the yellow and blue plastic insignia in his lapel, the door opened and long-legged Wolf Manheim came across the foyer.

The Secret Service man was gone and she and her quarry were vis-à-vis at last. As if in one of her own word pictures, she could see herself and the man facing each other like leader lions of rival prides. Both tall and lithe, except that he looked as if he had stepped out of a Gothic church window. "Too lean," she thought, "almost a beautiful death's head, or a concentration camp—of course, he was *in* a concentration camp as a child . . . but that was decades ago." Measuring herself, in her mind's eye, against his rangy frame and relishing the prospect of matching wits with the "geopolitical genius"—as the *Times* had referred to him—made her hunger for the *agon,* the combat of ideas that her interviews at their best were known for. "Max von Sydow!" she flashed, "that's who he reminds me of. Max, twenty-five years ago."

"I'll have tea, too. I admire the English," he said, and smiled slowly.

"Just like on television," she thought, and punched the ON button. She spoke in rapid, intelligent clips, wiggling her fingers in the air when quoting from a newspaper or report.

> B.J-R: Dr. Manheim, since Christmas the world situation is such that we hear, once again, frightened talk of World War III. You've seen today's New York *Times.* Richard Nixon's press conference at the Hotel Pierre to announce, for the fourth time in as many years, that "World War III has already begun," finally made the front page. And Henry Kissinger has let it be known that the situation is "more than serious." But the *Times* is riveted on what *you* are going to say, calling you the man closest to the President during this, quote, "low-grade panic," unquote. Are you, and is it?
>
> W.M.: I have always worked closely with the President. "Closest" is a subjective judgment that I can't make. Second—is there panic? Not that I can see. But then Congress hasn't returned from its holiday recess yet.
>
> B.J-R: No, and the Vice-President is being accused of waving the bloody shirt, milking the crisis before the first primaries. How serious is it? The President referred to "two fronts." How apt is that figure of speech? Why the war image—"fronts"?
>
> W.M.: Let's take the first "challenge," if you prefer. The President in his speech of December twenty-seventh stated that *"if"* Cuban agents were involved in the destruction of the American Embassy in Honduras and the subsequent insurgent violence, *"if"* these reports were true, *then* it could be characterized as a "warlike act." In relation to the second challenge, the Soviet ultimatum to the People's Republic of China regarding the offshore islands, our

position is that the United Nations should immediately dispatch observers to the area. I met with the Secretary General to that end, as you know, on Monday.

B.J-R: Why you instead of Secretary of State Higgins? Is it true that you are going to succeed him in that post sometime between your visit to China and the fall elections?

W.M.: I never speculate on such matters.

B.J-R: No, but your trip to the People's Republic of China is certainly going to be seen as a "tilt" toward the PRC and away from the USSR in the present confrontation.

W.M.: I don't see why. As soon as I return I will chair special meetings with Mr. Arbatov and the Soviet U.N. delegation in order to hear their side of the latest chapter in their long-standing dispute with the People's Republic.

B.J-R: If it's merely another "chapter" in a "dispute," then why the panic? The March Against War last Sunday in New York had over two hundred thousand people out in very cold weather . . . .

W.M.: What about it?

B.J-R: What has the rest of the world extremely jittery, Dr. Manheim, is the uncanny coincidence of nuclear war headlines and leaks. I mean the Los Angeles *Times* came straight out with a "Thinking the Unthinkable" headline on page one. *Time* and *Newsweek* both have issues going on the stands tomorrow—SINO-SOVIET SHOWDOWN—in covers printed in 1950s red, and Richard Harkin in the Washington *Post* writes this morning that World War III began in Iran when the hostages were seized . . . (Roman numeral III as if there could be a IV or V.) I mean, doesn't it appear that these leaks are designed to prepare the country for the ultimate?

W.M.: For the unthinkable?

B.J-R: Un*thinkable* but, apparently, not un-*do*able.

W.M.: I follow you. However, it all depends from where the leaks, uh, sprang—if that's the correct verb—because these kinds of headlines have in fact galvanized the *anti*war forces as nothing has since the height of the Vietnam crisis. If I weren't such a notorious east coast liberal I might ask Mr. Nixon's famous question: "Is it a liberal plot?"

B.J-R: Um . . . Look, do you mind if we come back to World War III next time? I feel that you're having a little fun or playing a small game before we—

W.M.: Just the opposite. You've won *two* Pulitzer prizes for your devastating "interviews"—if you can call the confession of broken men that—and more than one government has almost fallen after your famous presence in the palace . . . . Are you really the illegitimate granddaughter of Bertrand Russell? *You're* the star; I'm afraid of *you*. I'm serious. Ask Peter Wick. No, don't, he's petrified, too. You don't know your own reputation, the Secret Service detail cried like babies when they heard—

She threw back her honey-colored pelt of hair and laughed so loud that the two agents in the kitchen came poking around the corner to see what was up. "Broken men, eh? God, I didn't know you were so witty. I thought you had a sort of honorary or, ah, media wit like your old mentor Henry Kissinger, or a more, ah, popular wit (the story about his unzipping his fly *was* true, wasn't it?) like your predecessor, Dr. Brzezinski."

Now it was his turn to laugh. His lips were held straight but the large hazel eyes showed suppressed merriment. In the further room the aide, Wick, could be heard talking sibilantly on the telephone, but even in the relative quiet she couldn't make out any of the words. They looked at each other out of residual smiles. (Was it true, she suddenly wondered, that only the eyes reflected feeling, all the rest being only muscular reflex?) She met and sustained his bright-eyed gaze easily. Then she let her eyes move at will over his form, sculptured in the soft jersey of the jogging suit. He half-turned to see if the Secret Service men had returned to their coffee, then leaned forward to talk in a purposefully conspiratorial tone.

"Suppose I go for my run, and then when I lose the SS I come over to your place and we continue?"

"Is this off or on the record?"

"However you prefer, Ms. Russell."

"You may call me Dr. Russell . . . and I'll be waiting for you." The hand that jotted down and passed the suite number to the great man was steady and cool and warm as it brushed the President's "left hand."

2

WASHINGTON, D.C.—JANUARY 13, 1984
(FRIDAY NIGHT)

Betsy Jones-Russell was too restless to sit and wait for the National Security Adviser to jog around the entire hotel complex until he finally turned up at her door. As the last daylight sank she detoured across the bridge connecting Watergate East and South. "Bridge of Sighs," she thought at random, sniffing in cold, cutting air; "So many; I had not thought death had undone so many," her association going to T.S. Eliot, then to his poor wife. "My nerves are bad. Yes, bad. Stay with me." Lord Bertrand Russell (her grandfather, "B.R.") had tried to help the much younger Eliot, but the wife . . . Had B.R. slept with her? No. Yes.

Sighing on the Watergate Bridge of Sighs, thinking of how dark and cold it was, of how the orange-roofed Howard Johnson's across the street appeared almost human alongside the pyramid of glass and concrete that was the Watergate Complex. Was the Italian architect who had designed this fortress, with the American flag atop whipping in the winter wind, making a political statement in stone? Here, now, before her eyes was the Fountainhead: piles of slabs flung up to make two office structures and three apartment units. A mall of shops stretched out to the hotel toward which she was going, and around it, ribbing the entire complex, were stony rows of concrete teeth, gray-white incisors demarking every balcony with the swollen elliptical wedges that the Italian had designed. "Unreal city . . . I think we are in rat's alley . . ." She brooded in the cold, wishing she were home in her cozy Bury Street flat in London.

She stared at the late shoppers and early diners. America never ceased to amaze her. Not that she was an Americaphobe like her grandfather, B.R.—in fact, what she felt for the American middle class was closer to compassion. Since 1980 the savings rate had all but collapsed—no one *could* save, with inflation roaring—so they *bought.* Now, every day crowds gathered in front of banks to watch for the twice-daily postings of interest rates, so they could withdraw and *buy.* Hoarding was becoming a national religion; fights, then small riots, broke out briefly in supermarkets. In the ghettos, systems of barter had virtually replaced the old marketplace economy. "The nation is caught up in the Red Queen's Race," she wrote, referring to *Alice in Wonderland,* "forced to run faster and faster merely to remain in the same place."

As in the Great Depression, the unemployed were once again blaming and losing confidence in themselves. In Detroit a gang of unemployed auto workers had managed to breach security and wreck twenty-five of the new robots that could each do the mechanical work of five flesh and blood employees. She gritted her teeth at the spectacle of millions being sold new body odors, new body images, new automotive body extensions—being sold *themselves.*

The beautiful rich people and the power elite here in Washington —men like Manheim's aide Wick—were openly beginning to turn on the "ordinary" people. She had heard a glamorous Washington party-giver say that "when the average American walks, his knuckles graze the ground." This new civil-war mentality was being acted out by the poor in innumerable gestures of individual violence, much of it self-directed. Even now the Watergate Mall was lined with armed guards, some of them staring at her as she stood molded by the wind.

One of the reasons that the world and its pundits now looked to a nonelected official like Wolf Manheim for some saving grace was the near-burned-out quality of American leadership since Jack Kennedy. Crooks and born-again Bible salesmen and their loyal opposition, hairdressers combing their way through national problems. . . . On the "Dick Cavett Show" she had described America's First Republic "beginning with the Revolution and ending with the adoption of the Constitution; the Second ending with Lincoln's waging of the Civil War to preserve the Union; and the Third Republic, now seemingly grounding to a halt with a series of profoundly disquieting bangs and whimpers." Cavett had, uncharacteristically, said nothing.

Two policemen handcuffing a youth at the other end of the bridge caught her eye. Why couldn't the sociologists and national planners understand that youth, in America as in the rest of the world, was not only right but desperate. The relatively innocent morality of youth was a human treasure, too often despised and scoffed at. The fact that young people got cynical when they grew older didn't mean they were wrong. The major uprisings—in Iran, South Korea, South Africa, Central America, America—were made by young people between thirteen and twenty. In recent weeks, Miami, Kwangju, Capetown, São Paulo—four cities on four different continents spanning the globe—had been scenes of bloody riots. Thousands of young black *and* white students in Capetown had been rioting since late April, openly defying the white police. The demonstrators in São Paulo, Brazil, were young, too—mainly metalworkers who had mounted massive strikes against the tough measures by the new president.

What are the links? she asked herself. What did Capetown have to do with Miami, or Kwangju with São Paulo?

In all four cases, a dangerous combination of ingredients was present prior to the outbursts. All four cities had large young suppressed populations struggling in a stagnant economy; in all four, the present economic downturn was preceded by a period of relative boom; and in each city, police or military forces had responded to the rising discontent of the young with preemptive crackdowns.

Miami was no less vulnerable for being in the United States. The "Third World" in the human sense had come to America, bringing its volatile politics of poverty and youth with it. That was how she had to write about it, she thought.

Yes, she felt some sorrow for the big upset country "where nothing *really* worked except the military—like the USSR," she had written; and her people "forever optimistic but without enough hope." North America was sinking deeper and deeper into the clutches of gigantic transnational corporations that were beyond even government scrutiny, were often not even located in the United States. Yet there was a huge protest movement that could, from time to time, hold some of the streets if not elected office. It would take that movement, she speculated, and the locked-out young and old people to fill up the streets around the clock to slow down the war machine that had especially been cranking up in this country since 1981. It had seemed clear for months that "a shit storm was coming." Or worse: In Florida, Illinois, New Jersey, California, the Carolinas—American Nazi Party and KKK candidates were actually running ahead of the primary polls. Waves of anti-Semitism had surfaced in France and the U.S. to a lesser degree in 1980. Now they were truly taking on national proportions. Serious historians were alluding to an "American Weimar"; inflation still eating the psychological and fiscal heart out of the middle class, the dark current of despair and fear and, yes, loathing of the new waves of black and Latino and Asian immigrants. In her July 1983 essay she had asked the rhetorical question—"During the 1984 presidential election, which flag will fly—white or black or brown? With one of the potential candidates *openly* talking about 'starting over again' after a thermonuclear war . . . ."

The wind was getting nasty now, yet still she stood staring up at the shadowy pile of stone. This nervous-making architecture—would it be found someday, carbon dating fixing the year circa 1984? Every culture is famous for at most half a millennium. "Take me," she said to herself with a smile, "I'm probably the last of the Russell line, or if not, certainly of the 'Orwell line': Ah, well, at least no one can take away the few cubic centimeters inside my skull that are my inheritance outright." She pounded her hands together for warmth—the guards were watching her—but her color was high now against the whipping wind.

An elderly couple bundling along on the way to an early dinner stared as they stepped around the tall, striking woman standing as if frozen at the front of the bridge, staring up at the walls of surrounding balconies, moving her head high and low as if it were a camera. The wind had loosened a few strands of her hair out from under the wool cap, the scarf unfurled like a banner, the boots were planted on the walk as if she were defending the bridge on which she stood. The heavy coat sat on her like armor, the leather tape recorder and camera paraphernalia was strung shieldlike across her shoulder and breast.

They passed and looked straight into her face, cream white with wind-red highlights along the strong bone structure. "That's the awful woman from England, you know she was written up Sunday in the *Post*. The one we saw on TV that wrote the best seller interviewing famous men."

"Oh, Russell, Russell, the one who said that America was the name of a nervous condition. To hell with her. Talking like that at a time like this . . ." By this time the couple had arrived at their destination, the most expensive, garish restaurant in the long, crowded mall.

Individuals and groups, trudging toward cocktails against the sharp wind that had sprung up, began to recognize the young woman who stood staring up at the finned protuberances of the dirty white walls of the Watergate.

"Miss Russell? I'm a historian at Catholic University here and I think your books and interviews are magnificent . . . the beginning of a new understanding of the role of the leader in decision making—"

"Yes. Thanks. Bye." Young, rather sexy, she speculated, would it be fun to run after him and try to take him up to bed? I must stop using people. I've been collecting concupiscent cocks since Georgi left and where am I? In Washington bloody D.C. on the eve of . . . *something* close to war—no lover and no baby at thirty-four bloody years old. It would be sheer vanity to fuck that young man just to make me stop feeling the other feelings I have in this place at this time. Oh dear, he's walking back. And here comes that helicopter again. "Bye."

She began to jog toward the hotel as the full complement of lights flooded on. With the bright safety illumination, music from hidden speakers washed across the mall and blew with the wind over the chopping and across the cold arena between the hotel and apartment units. "Strike Up the Band," it felt good to run in the cold. Another dozen security guards had popped out of the dark doorways into the bright light of the total security. "Strike Up the Band, Boys! Directed and produced by Ayn Rand, copyright 1984." She was loping now, broken-field through the staring guards; startled, still-affluent visitors to the capital paused to stare, then continue on their way to dine on the lower level and along the mall.

In her rooms she hugged herself for warmth and knelt on the vinyl settee to look out the window at the reflecting fins and bright teeth of the surreal walls of the complex. Somewhere out there, beyond, in the dark, Wolf Manheim was jogging, the security contingent in tow, trotting in sunglasses behind, alongside, and ahead of his shadowy form. The National Security Adviser was, she knew, forty-eight, yet from the looks of him he was in peak physical condition, would make the Secret Service pant toward the end, glad to let them go for the night. A noted womanizer like Wolf Manheim must have a routine of some sort worked out with the sunglasses.

She thought again about his body. She knew sculpture, had an authentic feel for the thrust of a Brancusi, the sensuous statement of a Jean Arp, the immanence of a *David* or a *Moses.* She knew and liked the male body very much indeed. "Ah, the great and the small," she cracked to herself, trying to imagine Wolf Manheim naked. The image was coming together: of the bony thrust of the shoulders, the long legs, the small buttock, the high chest, the fine chestnut hair; she was just working down toward the flat belly and what she sometimes called "the life of the building" when the picture began to dim because she remembered that on the left or right forearm would be the old tattoo from Buchenwald. Or did they do that at Buchenwald? The next interview session would have to include the death camps.

As if under compulsion, her free-association to the camps was the need to have a child. The thought of war or torture or natural calamity somehow always sponsored in her a maternal longing, so that now in her imagination as there rose a blurred image of a huge ditch filled with bodies starved to skeletal abstraction, at the same time an imperative in her breasts and loins clamored for recognition. Then the ditch of corpses, the tragedy without God, would give way in her vision to a dim delivery room, soft music, Mozart, and a baby nursing at her breast sucking her to sleep. The baby looking like Bertrand Russell at birth (she could see the photograph, the infant in the dress of the 1870s). There was never a clear image of a man in these dreams. She had tried out various models. She should experiment with Wolf Manheim? . . . She pictured again the hungry infant, and rubbed her full breasts . . .

The muted buzz from the entry dispelled her vision entirely. He was leaning in the doorway, no Secret Service in sight, chest rising and falling evenly, short hair mussed like a boy's over the long, grave face. "I'm running every night like a stag pursued by the hounds of the Secret Service and I can't get below one-eighty, and you have this slim body. What's your exercise secret?"

"I occasionally smoke a cigarette by an open window."

He laughed in that straight-faced way, and so did she, mimicking him subtly. At 5' 10½" it was a pleasure for her to be able to look up at 6' 3". "You're very bony," she said, leading him into the dark apartment, "surely you don't need to be any leaner."

"Don't turn on the light," he said, "let's sit over here and take in the famous view."

"Isn't it incredible, the sheer incrumental mass of it—"

" 'Incru mental?' "

"Mm. Bloodless."

"You know you have a quite vocabulary. Why don't I interview *you?*"

"Ah, no, you're the clever one. I score the coup of the year, getting an interview with the man in the cockpit, at the locus of power in the midst of a crisis, then he jogs away from all the questions. I can't think why you broke your perfect record of 'deep background' leaks to grant me the pleasure of your company."

"Because, Dr. Russell—"

"Betsy, or B.J.R., or B.J., or—"

"—whatever, you're the best. I mean Sally Quinn's humor, and Barbara Walters's nerve, and Oriana Fallaci's brilliance, and then your—"

"Vocabulary, and my *body* and—"

"And when I read that you had let slip that you're Bertrand Russell's illegitimate granddaughter, that, I'd say, clinched it." The pale throw of the lights from the outer complex washed across their faces as they sat half in shadow. She felt a shared sense of energy or sex—"call it life," she thought, as one of the helicopters circled in front of their window.

"That did create a stir, didn't it? Would you like some juice or—"

"Never touch it."

"Full of vitamin C are you, Dr. Manheim?"

"In a manner of speaking. Wolf. And are you? The *illegitimate* granddaughter? Why did you absolutely refuse to talk to the media about it?"

"Look, I'm a tape recorder, not a star. Though I must say I'm rather bitter about the scatter shots hinting that I'm somehow the product, one generation removed, of some sort of cypripareunia."

"Now come on—"

"Oh, you know, Lord Bertrand Russell, siring an offspring with a prostitute—"

"And your being the offspring of the offspring?"

"That's it. As if B.R. needed to pay for it. It's too killing."

"Well, then, Betsy, what *is* the story? You can tell me, I won't breathe a word."

"So you're really a fan of Bertie Russell . . . What if I rewarded you for a 'frank exchange of views' with the untold story?"

She could see the play of animation on the window-lit part of his face. She knew that he was about to reach out to touch her. Her mind was lucid but deep in her she felt a spark, a flicker of flame. Then he winced and turned profile to stare out into the cold. Did he shudder or was it the refraction of the light? This was the globe-trotting mystery man, the "high source" that had eluded the media since his vault to power. Now he was slipping away again just as she thought that he was opening up to her.

"Betsy," he said abruptly, "I want to put my head in your lap."
Just like that. His gaze did not stray from the dark.

There was a curious, almost vulnerable note in his voice; what
the hell, why not? "If you'll talk."

She could not see his eyes as he swiveled around to rest his head
on her. She felt the weight of it in her crotch and had to catch her
breath. His long legs hung over the settee. "Don't worry," he said
softly, "I'm just ramfeezled." Which brought a throaty laugh from
her and her breathing returned to nearly normal.

"A lovely word. Are you exhausted from jogging? No. My God,
Wolf, don't tell me the war talk is . . ." He lay quietly, his head
heavy between her legs.

"We can talk a little about that—but not for the interview—later.
I just have these . . . headaches since I was a kid. This feels better.
Thank you."

"Oh. Since you were a child in the concentration camps? . . .
Sorry."

"You know about that?"

"Of course. I know everything *printed* about anyone I interview." She stroked his wide forehead, just brushing the temples
with her tapered fingers. His eyelids fluttered. She could feel throbbing. This was more than a headache. It was quiet and dark; she
leaned her head back on the bolster and closed her own eyes for a
moment, leaving her fingers curled in his hair. As if from her
dossier on him, the facts printed out on the blue void behind her
closed eyes while the helicopter revved up again.

WOLFGANG H. MANHEIM, SPECIAL ASSISTANT TO
THE PRESIDENT OF THE UNITED STATES FOR NA-
TIONAL SECURITY AFFAIRS. DIRECTOR OF THE RE-
SEARCH INSTITUTE ON INTERNATIONAL ORDER,
PROFESSOR OF HISTORY AND GOVERNMENT AND
A MEMBER OF THE SLAVIC INSTITUTE AT HAR-

VARD UNIVERSITY. A DIRECTOR OF WAR AND
PEACE STUDIES AT COLUMBIA UNIVERSITY.

BORN BERLIN, GERMANY, JANUARY 13, 1936. CON-
FINED TO BUCHENWALD CONCENTRATION CAMP
1944. LIBERATED BY ALLIES, JUNE 1945.

ADOPTED IN CHICAGO, ILL., BY FAMILY OF ATTOR-
NEY NICHOLAS C. KING, WINTER 1946. HONOR STU-
DENT THROUGH ST. JOHNS MILITARY ACADEMY.
B.A. AND M.A. UNIVERSITY OF CHICAGO, 1959.
PH.D., HARVARD UNIVERSITY 1961.

1962–1968, JUNIOR FELLOW AT INSTITUTE FOR WAR
AND PEACE, COLUMBIA UNIVERSITY. EDITOR,
JOURNAL FOR THE STUDY OF WAR AND PEACE,
1963–1968.

1969–1973, LIAISON TO THE NATIONAL SECURITY
COUNCIL.

1973–1976, AUTHOR OF THREE BOOKS AS PRIVATE
CITIZEN. VISITING PROFESSOR AT HARVARD AND
COLUMBIA.

1976–1979, ASSISTANT TO THE SECRETARY OF
STATE. 1980, EXECUTIVE DIRECTOR TRILATERAL
COMMISSION. 1981–1984, SPECIAL ASSISTANT TO
THE PRESIDENT. . . .

She drifted. The boldface lies—"I mean *type,*" she mused, "the
facts"—began to melt into a montage. The corner of her mouth
twitched. She had brought a thick folder of clips from the London
Times with her on the plane. Now they tumbled out, story after
picture after editorial about the tall medieval mystery man meeting

in Bonn, Teheran, Asslamibad, Paris, Beijing . . . his erudition, wit, his women, his awful childhood in the awful Buchenwald. The coverage of how the then former unknown—except to the National Security elite—had helped finesse the Shah of Iran out of the United States, thus starting the process of eventual release of the hostages. No one in the government had ever leaked the secret of how an unknown aide had managed this. The only leak had been the name, Wolf Manheim.

"The man that Henry Kissinger had dreamed of being," was said by columnist Mark Turbidy to have been Gore Vidal's assessment, "the man who had trumped Kissinger's ace, the Shah, with a joker that no one has yet seen." From the Hollywood underground came —"I've had them all and I can tell you that Henry and the rest of them were common clay compared to Wolf."

Betsy breathed suddenly and looked down. Wolf's head was moving but his body was almost rigid. His head rubbed back and forth across her mound, she knew she was wet. "Wolf, easy, are you all right?" She tried to steady his head with her fingertips. She felt him struggling up from some region until with a shuddering sigh he woke up and spoke to her, his diction now almost as clipped as hers.

"B.J-R.?" She could feel a mist of perspiration on his forehead, though there could have been no temperature change in a hermetically sealed suite at the Watergate.

"Redux?" she said.

He laughed. "Yes, I feel much better," though not sounding it. He turned his head toward her, reached up and ran a tapered finger along her jawline. His touch was gentle, evocative; she moved her fingers around his temples in little circular motions. She was feeling more at that moment than during any number of moments she could recall of actual sexual intercourse. "I'm sorry," she said softly, "about the headaches. They must be painful, you were sort of thrashing about."

"Well, but in your lap I've found more than redux—"

"Refreshment?"

"Thank you . . . sometimes it's worse. I lost an entire day to it after the crisis with the Shah."

"Are you lying to me again?"

"No."

"Do you want to talk about Buchenwald? Not on tape. I mean now? . . ."

"No thank you. No, I know you're not prying. You're a kind person, besides being a raging beauty—that old phrase fits you— and a champion talent: you've been kind to me. The CIA and Secret Service said you were a dangerous bitch?"

"What else did they say?"

"Just that you had seduced some of the famous men that you've interviewed . . ."

"I see. Tell me, does the CIA or Secret Service do anything for your headaches? No, I didn't suppose they did."

Before she could say anymore he reached up to touch her lips. He clearly wanted her to stop before she said something that would undo the moment. "Please," he said, "I want to talk to you. I respect you, maybe even trust you a little, which for me is probably a mistake. I'll be over this after a good night's sleep, then tomorrow night, if you'll have dinner with me, I'll tell you what very little I remember about Germany and the camp. Yes?"

"I like you like this, Wolf. Just *slightly* indisposed. Here you are almost at my feet, talking sensibly, answering questions. Prone like this I can mother you a bit, and you, claiming the eternal alibi— a 'headache'—don't have to mount your famous sexual onslaught." He chuckled again, but carefully, as if it might disturb his system or some delicate equilibrium that he had achieved with her there.

He could have been an actor, she reflected, gazing down at his pale face. His voice was low and rich: ". . . 'with my head in your lap. Did you think I meant *country* matters?' "

" 'I know not, my lord,' " she took the cue, stroking his hair. "You're the most awful womanizer. I *know* you were with three women, serially, last summer at The Hague, and with two simultaneously during the games at Milan. Shh. Don't say a word in your own defense, just rest here on your or, rather, *my,* former glories, or *your* laurels and my . . ."

He rubbed her belly with his cheek. "Former?" he asked. " 'Get thee to a nunnery!' You look like twenty-five, there's nothing 'former' about you."

"Thanks."

"Listen," he said, "before I go home to my cell I'd like one bedtime story."

"I'm tempted," she whispered. "You're a man who knows how to talk. That inspires trust. What story do you want to hear tonight?"

"Just a little one. Call it 'Lord Bertie Russell: the first ninety-eight years.' "

"Oh, lord, Wolf. Ha! My God, we'll be here all night. Look, I'll give you an abstract of all except the seven or so years that I actually knew him. But in return you must promise to tell me tomorrow night about the Shah, off the record, and *for* the record answer hard questions about these World War III rumors. Bargain?"

"Yes . . . am I too heavy?"

"No." She could feel him relax.

The truth was, she worried to herself, that the U.S. and the USSR might, this time, actually *be* on a collision course. Wolf Manheim had been reported locked into the National Security Council eighteen hours a day, and when he wasn't there he was huddling with the President at Camp David. "No comment," and the entire world waited while the media camped in the halls and dogged his steps. She had told the London *Times* that it was foolish for her to stay in Washington, during a world crisis, hoping to see the man *least* accessible. Then had come the announcement that the President's emissary, Wolfgang H. Manheim, would meet, separately, with officials at the highest levels of both the USSR and the PRC. And *then* she had been telephoned to stand by for an *eight-hour* interview, as she had requested. London was ecstatic.

She had no scrambled telephone to London, and she knew that the editors had to realize that Manheim, the U.S. government, was going to use her, her interview, to say something important, indirectly. It was an old trick. Especially on the eve of war. But he didn't seem to be doing that. So far he had said nothing directly pertaining to U.S. concerns in the Far East or the hot spots in Central America. Tonight, alone, she had thought he would give her a "background" bombshell. When that didn't materialize she had assumed that he would suggest sex. Instead he had presented an entirely different side of himself: simple, sincere, almost boyish. The sexual urge she had felt for him had not evaporated; instead a current of tenderness had been born tonight and now the sexual hunger was intertwined with another, rarer feeling. Not just her loins but her heart had been somehow touched by this contradictory man-myth who, unlike other of the media's mystery men, really was difficult to define. "All right," she began, "an off-the-record bedtime fable for a good National Security Adviser."

As she began her voice was intimate but clear with no trace of bathos, typical of the Russell family, past hope or fear, combined with a cheerfully tragic vision of things. She was a good storyteller, she believed, because Russell had been her master, and so now she commenced her tale just as if the dim hunks and shapes of hotel furniture were looming around the drawing room, crouching beyond the firelight, waiting to be included in the telling.

"Well . . . his life spanned, in U.S. terms, the period between the presidencies of Ulysses S. Grant and Richard Nixon, 1872 to 1970. Before my grandmother had even met him he had written the *Principia Mathematica;* he was about to go to prison for resistance to the Great War and to divorce his first wife, the Quaker beauty Alys Pearsall Smith. Right, that takes us to 1914 . . .

"His affair with another great beauty, Ottoline Morrell, had reached serious proportions, and he took an offer from Harvard to come to the States in order to find a perspective—regarding both love and war. So he was settled in at Cambridge, Mass, to teach at Harvard. Of course, he was a devoted Anglophile—though that changed considerably later, as you know, in your time—and wrote his mistress that the club where he stayed was 'dirty and disgusting, a regular American place' and that the men were 'hard, efficient, unmeditative.' He thought highly of the Harvard faculty but was always ambivalent about the American 'character.' At Harvard he met the young T.S. Eliot, who was his student, whom he described as 'well dressed and polished.' Now be patient, because we are approaching my grandmother, who, you will be the first to learn, was—American!

"Having sworn you to secrecy, I will tell you on 'deep background' that Russell visited the nineteen-year-old woman—who would by 1920 give birth to my mother—in your own adopted city of Chicago in May of 1914. Her father was a doctor, a gynecologist. They say that while he was a 'freethinker' in theology, in morals he was a rigid puritan. B.R. said the man was 'ravaged' by sexual repression. Dr. Jones, this pillar, then, was my maternal great-grandfather. You're following me? The good doctor and his wife, whoever she was, begat my grandmother.

"Her name was Helen Jones, and she had studied at Oxford. She had met Russell there and invited him to stop at her parents' mansion when he made his tour of the States. According to family legend, B.R. was the perfect house guest. Helen set her two younger sisters to guard the stairs while she and Bertie made love in the guest room. He wrote his English mistress that he had met a young lady 'of considerable literary talent.' Then he sailed for home . . .

"Back at Trinity College, Cambridge, he wrote to Helen: 'Ah God! to see the branches stir / Across the moon at Grantchester.' So, naturally, she was determined to come to England to marry him. She arrived in August of 1914 and B.R. wrote in his diary that she had interesting, Chinese-shaped brown eyes—my mother did too, but not me, mine are just blue and round—and that she had a good figure and a passionate temperament. Well, the war fever was up, and B.R. became completely involved along with Shaw and the others in nonviolent resistance to it. Poor Helen Jones followed him around the country actually begging, he wrote, to be allowed to be his mistress. Of course, he had been scrupulously honest with her as he was with all his women over the whole eighty-odd years of his active sex life . . .

"The years passed. Bertie went to jail, wrote books, articles, pamphlets—'man is the product of causes which had no prevision of the end they were achieving; that his origins, his growth, his hopes and fears, his loves and his beliefs, are but the outcome of accidental collocations of atoms' . . ."

Wolf spoke up for the first time since she had started the story —" ' . . . that no fire, no heroism, no intensity of thought and feeling, can preserve an individual life beyond the grave; that all the labors of the ages, all the inspiration, all the . . .' what?"

". . . 'all the noonday brightness—' "

"That's it—'all the noonday brightness of human genius, are destined to extinction in the vast death of the solar system, and the whole temple of Man's achievement must inevitably be buried beneath the debris of a universe in ruins . . .' Do you know that we had to memorize that in graduate English at Chicago along with 'Unto the Last' and the mad scenes from *Lear?* But it's fantastic to have his life at your fingertips—ah, your fingertips, that feels so good—and his words, you must be writing a book. You—"

"Shh. I am. It's called *Descent* and nobody but you and my publishers know."

"I'll never tell."

"The new book is my baby, shared with no one so far. Its center-piece will be an interview with Bertie begun in 1966 and carried on until the month of his death."

"Could I have a look at—"

"Maybe. If you're terribly sweet about recognizing the claims of history and cooperating with me at tomorrow's session—"

"Then, as a compromise, why don't I take a few pages with me?"

She laughed as loud as she could with him on her lap. "What a diplomatic child you are. I tell you what—I have some transcript handy from '67 to '68 you can look at. Up, boy, up!"

She darted into the bedroom, half hoping he'd follow. She called back to him, "The first part of this was published in the *Times* several years ago and my career, as they say, was really launched."

"You were in Wales with him then. Did he actually believe that an atomic attack was imminent?"

"Here you are. Next chapter tomorrow night, *after* our taping session."

"No, you can't talk about a 'universe in ruins' and tomorrow in the same breath. You said yourself that this World War III talk had you upset. Remember, that quotation ends with something about . . . despite ultimate extinction that we must live 'constantly in the vision of the good.' So . . ."

"So?"

"So, keep going. Your illegitimate mother is, I guess, about to be conceived."

"Clever aren't you? You might have a future in diplomacy. All right. It was three years and several women later. B.R. had been to prison, the war had devoured Europe, changed everything. Now all this time Miss Helen Jones had been living in B.R.'s Bury Street flat in London—I have it now. Bertie was divorced by this time, so Helen's hopes still burned bright as ever. He only saw her on rare occasions—he was traveling—and felt guilty about that. He thought she had become more than a little strange and her literary output was uneven, sometimes chaotic. How she must have loved him . . . B.R. was one of those men, physically and mentally radiating life force; the greatest *mind* of his time, one of the most vital of *any* time . . .

"Well, in 1918, Helen gave birth to their daughter, called Cordy Jones, after King Lear's daughter Cordelia. Helen, my grandmother, was committed to a private sanitorium in 1919, and the child, Cordy, was raised by Dr. and Mrs. Jones in Oak Park, Illinois. Cordy, my mother, lived in America until 1937, then she ran away to fight with the George Orwell contingent in the Spanish Civil War. And now we really must stop for tonight so I can go to the loo and you can go home and pick up your messages from the President."

"No—"

"Yes! To be continued tomorrow night after—"

"After dinner."

"After a taping session. Here, sit up . . ."

When she reentered the room he was standing, lanky, in the dark near the door. "You've made my evening," he said softly. Somehow, she didn't feel like being clever, just wanted him to enclose her gently in his arms, but she didn't move.

"You'll tell me the rest, everything, from your mother and George Orwell right up to *his 1984.*" It was somewhere between a question and prophecy, his voice was clear and low, seductive without, perhaps, meaning to be. It was an American voice, except that the diction, she had noted, had a foreign edge to it from time to time.

She stepped to him to take his hand and lead him to the door, or bedroom? To the door. In the light from the corridor the bone structure of his face stood out in relief, his eyes lost in shadows. "Happy birthday," she said quietly.

"You *have* done your homework," he said after a long moment.

"Oh, yes. No party? No, ah, 'friend' to celebrate with you?"

"No. Just you. Tomorrow night."

"Right. Good night, Wolf. Happy birthday."

He smiled and as he turned away she caught that glimpse of hauntedness again in the eyes. She stood in the doorway and watched him walk away with his shoulders slightly hunched. She felt a tenderness—that caught her off guard—for those bunched and powerful shoulders. She shut the door as he turned the corner to the elevators. Wolf Manheim pushed the DOWN button, then pressed his temples with the heels of his hands and uttered a silent prayer that the nightmare, as if it were a thing alive, would spare him tonight.

BUCHENWALD—JANUARY 13, 1944

" . . . Son, keep your voice down . . . Because I am the 'Hospital Kapo' and you are my son. And because we are not Jews, we are German; and we are Communists, that is why we wear red stars instead of yellow ones. We are Communists and we run Buchenwald. You'll see what I mean by 'run.' Then, after, you will have your birthday party."

Dr. Manheim gave a sighing laugh and tightened his grip on the boy's, Wolfgang's, hand. As they stepped out, as if on cue the loudspeakers began to blare Offenbach's "Grave Dance." It was a clear and unseasonably warm winter Sunday afternoon and eight-year-old Wolfgang felt both fear and awe as he half trotted to keep up with the commanding figure of his father. Wolf was glad now that he had stood up to Colonel Hoder, his stepfather, and demanded to go live with his real father again. As he strode along, the doctor pointed out the sights, using his entire hand the way someone else would point a finger. The doctor's hands were wide and potent looking to the skinny boy. Everything about the leading

39

inmate of Buchenwald struck the boy as potent: round bald head, bright and freckled skin, barrel chest, wedge shoulders. Still cutting, in his loose camp garb, the figure of the Berlin professor and doctor that he had been.

"Wolfgang, see there. In 1939 when I first came, there was a beautiful stand of timber right inside the compound. You could go in there on a Sunday like this and sit and see the whole Thuringian countryside—see, there, between the watchtowers, through the barbed wire."

The boy, looking dutifully, could see the hazy outlines of the Harz Mountains in the distance with the double line of Kyffhäuser peaks cutting through the clouds. A farmer plodded along behind a plow and team—that was in the middle distance—and further on the boy could make out the village, its roofs and spires, and chimneys curling up purple smoke. Because of the Offenbach he could not hear the Sunday church bells, but he knew they were ringing. "Do *they* know that we are here?" he asked his father. The doctor looked down with a strange smile across his broad face.

"Your mother, may she rest in peace, always liked to believe that the Germans round about here knew something but 'not everything' . . . But she was not, like me, a Marxist. She was a Social Democrat, I suppose, if she was anything." He spoke as if to an adult and the boy's round eyes did not register. With this, the big man bowed with something that the boy in memory later would realize was irony.

"Now, those are the guard towers, of course—don't look up. That is the Riding Hall, I tell you about that later, it's for Commandant Koch's wife. That, there, is the stable. Let's go over this way and watch the game. That is the motion picture theater, yes, and there they are building a—you know what a *maison de rendez-vous* is?—never mind."

Past the crematory, without saying anything, the doctor, so much heavier than the other prisoners, led the boy along. The boy, though slender, was not emaciated either, and his face had color; that was rare in this camp of dead-white masks.

Beyond the Headquarters Area was an improvised soccer field. Two teams were hard at it and a small crowd of inmates cheered and called as the many-legged action flashed back and forth. When Manheim, father and son, stood to watch, red- and green-badged inmates around the doctor bowed to him; even several SS in attendance smirked in recognition. Wolfgang's eyes were opened even wider at the sight of the neatly cut and patterned uniforms of the players and their spiked shoes. That's what he wished above all that he could have for his birthday. He looked up to ask but his father was looking down with his lips pursed in a signal of silence and one round eye closed in a wink of complicity.

The players stopped for their rest period and the doctor began to lead the boy through the crowd toward the "zoo." Wolfgang's gaze danced from color to color on the inmates' clothing: a riot of markings and colors and geometrical shapes. His father explained it all to him with great authority as they walked through the crowd of deferential scarecrows, their rictus grins a sign of Dr. Manheim's importance. The boy basked in the reflected glory, only half understanding the lecture. The tides of the Offenbach continued to flow over one and all; that and the sparkling sunshine seemed to animate the scene as on a jerky piece of high-contrast film.

". . . serial number on the left breast, prisoner designation, the triangles, on the right trouser leg. (At Auschwitz the number is tattooed on the left forearm of the prisoner—you know about Auschwitz? About the Jews? No? Never mind.) Red is the color for the political prisoner, like us; second offenders wear a stripe above the triangle, like that man, see—Good afternoon, Mr. Kantor, lovely weather, isn't it—Jehovah's Witnesses wear purple (stay away from them, and from the criminals, they wear green, and from the *Lumpenproletariat,* they wear black, and from the homosexuals, see there, they wear pink, in fact you don't talk to *anyone* but the people at the hospital that I tell you).

"There, now the gypsies wear the brown triangle. Now the Jews: they must wear an extra yellow triangle pointed up, see, and that plus the yellow one pointed down makes the six-pointed Star of David. Now those who violate the race laws, you know, if they . . . marry someone not of their race, they must wear a black border around their green or yellow triangle. The foreigners are the ones with the letters printed on their triangle—F for France, B for Belgium, and so forth. *(Bonjour, monsieurs, trez plaisant, et le soccer et trez competetive, non?)* Then there are the Ks, that's for the *Kriegsverbrecher,* the war criminals, but you won't find any here. Those who wear white As, for *arbeiten,* go right through with the Ks to Auschwitz. Where were we? Yes. The penal colony have a big black dot over their triangles. Anyone suspected of planning an escape has a red-and-white target sewn or painted on his chest and back. And last are the feeble-minded, with the word moron on the armband. It's a theater, it's a circus, Wolfgang. There's one poor bird here who is a Jew, who is a member of the Jehovah's Witnesses, a 'race defiler' and a repeat offender *and* wears the escape target. A *rainbow,* the man's a human rainbow of color."

Wolfgang was assured that beyond the soccer field was something more fascinating for a birthday boy. It required special permission even to go near it, but Dr. Walter Manheim had told his "colleague," SS Major Dr. Ding-Schuyler, that he must have the permission to take his young son—who had just lost his mother—to the "Falcony Court." They circled the crowd and headed toward the south end of the camp.

"That's Weimar, in that direction," he pointed to distract his son. The doctor did not want Wolfgang to pay any notice to the boxing match that was taking place beyond the soccer and volleyball events. Every time the doctor saw the guard's darlings, the young criminals stuffed with black-market food, with their bulging biceps, he wanted to scream with rage. The sight of the young bulls punching and prancing in the ring while the audience of skeletons cheered them on, hysterically, with their last iota of energy, always drove the doctor into a fury, a state he could ill afford in this place.

The Headquarters Area which father and son now approached included administration facilities, five SS officers' residences with large gardens, hothouses, landscaped parks and clubs and the zoological gardens, all walled off from the restricted armories and war plants. Here the streets were balanced and paved, all was clean, trim, freshly painted, manicured, scrubbed. "The swamps have been drained. Here we are," he said, and nodded to a pair of SS men, who stopped them to look at their passes and then returned to their cigarettes and gossip.

The Falconry Court had been built as a tribute to Hermann Göring "at a cost of over 135,000 marks," the father said, "for the building materials alone. But the Reich-Huntsman-in-Chief, Herr Field Marshal Göring, has never even set eyes on it." The doctor shook with silent laughter, Wolfgang watching, and hugged the boy's shoulders.

They walked quickly through the clear air, under the brisk sky. The Offenbach was behind them, and now they could hear the gay waltz melodies of a live orchestra. "That's the little theater on your right. There are actors, an orchestra and wonderful, authentic costumes for the plays. You've been to the children's theater in Berlin?"

The barrel-chested doctor continued to point out the sights on this bizarre birthday journey. The ancient-looking Teutonic falcon house, carved in massive oak planes. The hunting hall, "everything hand-carved, inside and out, no expense spared—ten fireplaces, great bear rugs." The falconers' and guards' domiciles, now housing notables like the French premier Leon Blum and other names the boy had never heard. Then, at last, they arrived at the game preserve.

The boy's eyes widened to see the caged wild cats, foxes, wild

boar. Beyond were pheasants, deer, roebucks, all grazing or walking as if in a state of nature. "Before," said the doctor, "there was
even a rhinoceros." Then the brown bears and wolf cages, "4,000
marks per wolf." The wolves lay as quiet as dogs, the peace of the
place under blue sky seemed to have put a spell on all the inhabitants of the little medieval world that stretched out around Manheim and son. (No way that the child could guess how Jews were
dragged here to be thrown into the bear's cage to be dismembered
and devoured by the huge beasts; the doctor had definite ideas
about how and when to tell the boy the truth.)

Finally, they came to the prize of the zoological gardens—the
Java monkeys. All the animals were well fed, the boy could see,
with shiny coats and bright eyes. "Why not," said the doctor, "they
get meat, honey, cereal, jam, mashed potatoes, even white bread."
He did not add that the precious foodstuffs were snatched from the
caches of the starving inmates. Indeed, to the boy, the doctor as he
strode along reminded him of a big, well-fed bear, and he was happy
for the first time in weeks. He was glad that Colonel Hoder, his
stepfather, had bowed to the doctor's demands to send the boy here
to Buchenwald so that he could be with his real father. If only
his mother could have lived so that they could all be together
again . . .

They walked back to the hospital, where Wolfgang was to see his
new living quarters, by way of the Sachsenhauser section. There,
the boy learned, the famous prisoners lived in small plain houses.
At the window of one such cottage the boy could see a fallen face
peering. "Another general out of favor with the Führer," said the
doctor, quickening his step so that the boy had to trot to keep up.
The strains of the Strauss waltz fell away behind them.

After Wolfgang's birthday party that night in the quarters of the
Sonderkommando, the death detail, the doctor explained to the
tired boy in words he could only partly understand the economics

of the world of the camp. How some of the inmates ate and drank the finest meat and schnapps and brandy while the others were worked to death as no beasts had ever been worked—he did not touch that night on the complex class distinctions of the camp nor on the details of the work of the Death Commando. Neither did he expatiate on the refinements of murder and torture which were the actual reasons for the camp's existence, or on the special distinctions between Germans and Jews in this new universe. He only repeated, "Remember you're a Communist, not a Jew."

In the hall of the *Sonderkommando* the music was Mozart from a recording by the Berlin Symphony Orchestra. And there were books—Marx, Freud, Reich, even Dickens, whom Wolfgang had been starting to read at home in English—books pulled from the trembling hands of incoming prisoners. Father and son had walked unchallenged past SS who were smoking and talking as if on ordinary guard duty, past rich-quilted, clean and comfortable sleeping quarters, showers and a first-aid station.

Inside, the Death Commando inmates were eating and drinking from a buffet as if a permanent birthday party were in progress. There were fine cheeses on the long table, fish, meat and real fresh bread, chicken, jam and butter and pastries, and on another sideboard cognac, brandy, wine and beer. The *Sonderkommando* all wore clean striped uniforms and yellow Stars of David.

The men crowded around the doctor to shake his hand and be introduced to the boy. A plate was piled high for him, his health was drunk. *Prosit!* He could hardly keep his eyes open. The impressions of the day, the rich food, the little glass of wine—he wanted to sleep. Then they all sang the birthday song to him and some even kissed him good-bye. The boy did not need to know that night that men of the *Sonderkommando,* like certain summer moths, lived only thirty days.

Outside, it had turned cold and dark. The big man lifted Wolfgang up and carried him in his arms, talking softly to him, telling him the few things he needed to know until tomorrow and his "new life at the hospital." Then Manheim stopped and pointed out to the boy where a great oak had once stood. "Goethe's oak, it was called, because the master used to come here to these mountains." And he bowed his massive shoulders in a gesture of irony as he began the verse. When the child's light, sweet voice chimed in, he stopped and let Wolf go on by himself.

> *Über allen Gipfeln*
> *Ist Ruh,*
> *In allen Wipfeln*
> *Spürest du*
> *Kaum einen Hauch . . .*

> O'er all the hilltops
> Is quiet now,
> In all the treetops
> Hearest thou
> Hardly a breath;
> The birds are asleep in the trees:
> Wait; soon like these
> Thou too shalt rest.

In the dark the big man wept silently and the boy laid his head on the heavy shoulder and slept.

4

WASHINGTON, D.C.—JANUARY 14, 1984
(SATURDAY)

BETSY JONES-RUSSELL: Dr. Manheim, this morning's editions of the New York *Times* and the Washington *Post* quote you as follows: "The question of tactical nuclear weapons arises automatically in the case of any serious threat to American vital interests," referring to yesterday morning's briefing to the Congressional delegation at the White House. And ABC News is quoting "a high source" to the effect that "the fuse is burning from Thailand to the Persian Gulf." Are you that "high source" (the style is certainly yours), and what is that figure of speech supposed to mean in plain language and what has it to do with tactical nuclear weapons?

WOLFGANG MANHEIM: I'm sure that "question" will have to be edited for publication, but I'll try to take up the main points. As you know, the "Carter Doctrine" of 1980 was a clear signal to the Soviets that if their Afghanistan invasion should overflow into the oil region of the Persian Gulf, then the United States would exercise a series of unspecified but serious options in order to protect her "vital interests" and, I might add, the vital interests of her allies in Western Europe and Japan. The Russians did not push forward, but within eighteen months Soviet-supplied North Vietnamese armies began to cross at will from their Cambodian, Kampuchean, puppet-controlled areas into Thailand. This continued until the Thais, at the beginning of the dry season, announced that they were prepared to invoke their defense pacts with the United States and China. The Soviet response, as you know, was to reassert its commitments to the Vietnamese. With this statement, the new crisis became a fact of life.

B.J-R.: And what has this to do with nuclear weapons, Mr. Source? And how did the "fire that is burning" start?

W.M.: As to the Sino-Soviet confrontation, you must go back to the 20th Party Congress in Moscow, in 1956—hold on, who is it? O.K. Better take a short break, B.J., we have the White House on the line. Please have—

" . . . some tea. —Was that your story from the London *Times* in the *Post* this morning?"

"No comment. Let me see it."

January 15, 1984

REALISTIC RADIO DRAMATIZATION STIRS
FEARS OF NUCLEAR ATTACK ON CAPITAL
FROM THE LONDON *TIMES*

WASHINGTON—Shortly after 9 A.M. Friday, while Washingtonians digested the news of the developing world crisis, a group of federal employees sat in an office across from the White House, sipping coffee and eating pastry.

Suddenly, a portable radio crackled with an urgent message: "The United States is under attack! This is not a test. The United States is under attack!" The announcement, over WPFW-FM, was accompanied by the sound of wailing sirens and honking cars.

Panic stricken, twelve of the workers stumbled down to the basement bomb shelter while three others—all employed at the federal volunteer agency ACTION—frantically turned the radio dial for more information.

"My first thought was 'This is it,' " ACTION information officer Les Wexler said. "It sounded totally realistic."

"Everyone else ran down to the basement," recalled Mark Walker, who said the announcement numbed him. "I ran up to the ninth floor to spend the last seconds with a few close friends. I kept watching the window for the mushroom cloud over Washington."

Then Walker turned on another radio and discovered the nuclear nightmare was not real.

"I heard that traffic was fine on Key Bridge, two window washers were trapped and there was a sale on at Sears," he said. "I figured it was a misunderstanding. I felt rather foolish. Some of us were almost hysterical."

What Walker and the rest of the ACTION employees had heard was part of a taped dramatization of the effects of nuclear war, broadcast as a paid announcement to promote anti-nuclear demonstrations set for today in the nation's capital. . . . Shades of Orson Welles . . .

She smiled slightly and stretched. There seemed to be only two Secret Service men inside the suite today and the Filipino cook never left the kitchen, but Captain America, as she had taken to calling Agent James Jarrell to herself, was as ubiquitously in evidence as ever. "Tea with milk?"

"Lovely. Thank you, Mr.—?"

Jarrell's reflecting sunglasses gave nothing away. The thin red lips jerked and recovered, then the tight ass of the young official disappeared around the corner and into the kitchen. He's too young to have been in Vietnam, she decided. She relaxed, thinking "thin-lipped like an albino gorilla, and a hard ass like a ferret." Her cheeks contracted as when one thinks of a lime or lemon and she closed her eyes not even trying to hear what Manheim was saying to the White House. If it *was* the White House . . . The man was nearly impossible to interview. What should have been the plum of her career thus far had, during this crisis, failed to produce more than two stories that were usable.

Wolf strode out of the working den, followed closely by his chief aide. "Off the record—student and public reaction," he said. Peter Wick looked surprised but kept on toward the toilet; Wolf looked up at the bending Secret Service man with the tea. "Jim, I'm going to be staying on here with Ms. Russell for a working dinner. After you've dropped it off, you gentlemen can relax in the security lounge, and I'll talk to you by phone around midnight. Tell Lee to get some rest before the trip. Peter? I'll talk to you tomorrow morning. Get some rest. There'll be no declaration of war tomorrow—Sunday's a poor news day. You don't approve? Peter, I'm just showing off a little for our famous guest. Ms. Russell, may I order for both of us?" The two agents filed out deadpan. A police helicopter droned by. "Jim, wait."

At first Wolf wasn't sure why she was laughing, then he remembered how much she hated the entire Watergate scene and began to laugh hard, too. *"The ambience,"* he blurted out over the noise.

"Ah, the *ambience, el ambiente,"* she subsided, knowing, somehow, that Jarrell would understand Spanish. *"You* order for *me?* Thanks anyway, doctor. Let's see—Jim, is it? The local restaurants are pretty famous for their cuisine, sooo, I think I'll just have a bacon and egg on whole wheat, and nothing to drink. May *I* order for *you,* Dr. Manheim?"

Jarrell began to jot down the food order. "Of course," Wolf said.

"He'll have the same, Jim, and a bottle of pilsner—"

"Erlangers."

"Yes, Erlangers—it would be. So will I, Jim. And you can put it on my account if you're going to the Mall." That stopped the gun hand mid-word, so that the National Security Adviser had to usher the agent out with a few whispered reassurances. Wolf turned back from the corridor with the most generous smile she had seen on the high-boned face yet.

"Let's get back to work, please, Wolf," she said, restarting the tape. "What's happening with the protests and—"

"Betsy, I can't, turn it off. The President wants no comment on the protests for the record until after Monday's cabinet meeting. So, off the record."

She sighed with only partly mock disgust and spread her arms akimbo. "The last news I heard was that there was a full-fledged uprising at the University of California in Santa Barbara."

"Yes," he nodded and unknotted his red-and-blue-striped tie as he got up. "More tea? I'm going to have some." He called out the news, from the kitchen. "They've burned the main drag of Isla Vista. The Los Angeles Sheriff's Department is alleged to have killed three students. There's going to be hell to pay as soon as the story moves on the wires, if we can't hold it until after Monday. This water's—"

"Hold it! Are you talking about instituting censorship? What the hell is going on, Wolf?"

"You hold it, B.J. Thank God tomorrow's Sunday and this thing —"

"Tomorrow is certainly Sunday and the Alliance for Survival is predicting that their Fifth Avenue march may go as high as five hundred thousand people. And I've half a mind to get out of here and join them." She rose and switched on two lamps, then paced to the window to watch the winking retreat of another official helicopter of some sort. She sensed him standing behind her before she felt his hand stroke down the back of her cashmere vest and stop just at the waist. "I'm not accomplishing anything here," she finished.

"Betsy, would I be planning to spend the *evening* with you if we were on the verge of a national emergency? You're not naive."

She turned away from the darkened window to face him. He was in his shirtsleeves now and his eyes were wide and warm. "No, I'm not naive. The media are aware from 'sources' that you are conducting a series of extended interviews with the London *Times* and that there has been no change in your plans to take a delegation to China next week, so of course the conventional thinking is that this little bout of cold war is nothing more than a combination of election year politics and Sino-Soviet saber rattling."

"Precisely."

"Precisely. Except the major media and the conventional wisdom are *nothing* if not naive. The students don't believe that this is just another 'Olympics War,' the people marching tomorrow in New York and a dozen other cities don't believe it, and I'm not sure that I believe it any longer."

He was going to kiss her, she knew, when someone rat-tapped at the door. "Jim?"

Jim Jarrell said that he had forgotten the beer, so they washed the bacon and eggs down with hot tea and the last of the milk. "I'll get you some more in the morning," he said quickly.

She decided not to rise to that presumption, if it was that. ". . . Now look, Wolf, let's level, as they say. On Wednesday the President read a little word-salad to the public about America's vital interests being threatened again by the 'deterioration in Soviet-Chinese relations,' and that you will fly to Beijing shortly. Thursday and Friday there were teach-ins on campuses all over the country. Then we have the overnight *Times* story on 'reserving the right to use, etc.' Today we have or should have the news from California of the worst domestic violence since Kent State and all of urban Florida under martial law. And what is the reaction of Dr. Wolfgang Manheim to all this? The youthful *éminence grise* to the White House, the big brain of Western geo-politics, that lithe jogger and man about town? Why, it's to suddenly grant an eight-hour interview to that dangerous Russell bitch. Then follows biographical bedtime stories and 'sorry, no oral history tonight, dear, I have one of my headaches,' and today we have a little supper and chat about laying in milk for the morning and, I have no doubt, the funny papers as well. Now you tell *me* who's naive?"

He studied her over the rim of his brown tea mug. She stared back, focusing on the cheek bones and prominent brow, not wavering. His eyes fell first. He sipped, then began talking in a loud voice, "Let's see what we can get on the FM music station."

"No." But his gesture stopped her as he took two long strides to the console. It was a Sondheim medley. He circled back and whispered in her ear—"bugs"—took her cool, slim hand, led her into the sleeping-den and shut the door. She watched him tune on the portable to the same station, only louder, then clean up the desk area for her to sit. With another gesture, he left the room and she could hear him collecting the tea tray. Her glance took in the small double bed, the locked wall files, the rich Iranian rugs, the crowded bookshelf over the bed, the rocking chair and the prints of concentration camp inmates on the wall by Käthe Kollwitz . . . or were they prints? Now he was back, laying out their cups and the pot on the desk and putting the rocker over close to her straightback desk chair. He sat looking calmly at her again, as if all the cloak-and-dagger business had not been his idea. When he did finally speak, the tone was low and resonant.

"I'm going to tell you what I know, Betsy. It *is* serious. How serious? Well, we don't know, that's why I'm going to talk to both the Chinese and the Russians next week. If you want to come along on the plane to Beijing, we can discuss that, too. It can be arranged. So, let's talk about a scale from one to ten—whether or not you agree with my estimations—for what it's worth. If the Cuban missile crisis was a seven, and Vietnam five, and Afghanistan six, then this is bigger—maybe seven and a half."

"With ten being the end?"

"With ten being the end."

"I see." She put her cup down and folded her hands between her legs like a little girl. "Worse than the missile crisis? Why? Because the Chinese make it a nuclear triangle this time?"

"That's a good way of putting it. The U.S. is at the apex of that triangle. If we tilt or are *perceived* to tilt, then the Soviets may unleash nuclear-tipped SORV rockets on China's nuclear installations or, conversely, the People's Republic of China will overrun all Southeast Asian borders and order its own population underground."

"Wolf, what do you mean 'tilt'? You've been pouring sophisticated weapons secretly into China since 1980—"

"How do you—"

"Wolf, I have my sources, and if I know it, the Soviets certainly do."

He turned the mug back and forth with tense fingers. "Listen," he said, "nothing we have given the PRC, *nothing,* has affected the balance of power vis-à-vis the PRC and the USSR."

"I'd like to accept that. I don't know why, but I would. Will the Kremlin?"

"You know their Washington man, Georgi Arbatov, what do you think?"

"Yes, I know him. I've interviewed him . . . I don't know, Wolf."

"They'll have to."

"Then why did the President say that you were flying to Beijing and not Moscow?"

"Because Beijing is now a U.S. favored nation and we're still not talking to the Soviets because they're sponsoring aggression in the Middle East and Southeast Asia and threatening the border with Thailand. And because we want to talk to Arbatov here, away from the bomb-throwers in the Kremlin."

"I know the party line," she said. "Why is everybody talking about Thailand and Southeast Asia when the real trip-wire is Egypt and the Middle East? Isn't it?" His face betrayed nothing beyond what he had said. She stretched her legs, long and shapely in opaque dancer's tights. "Do you *want* me to go along to Beijing?"

"Yes." He got up to change stations, then stopped as the news summary on the hour started up.

> ... in Boston, comedian Dick Gregory, still at it, told a Harvard University rally that the United States was so weak that it was, quote, egging on Russia and China to destroy each other. Gregory announced that he was collecting the signatures of notables who would begin a hunger strike if the United States did not back the United Nations demand for immediate Sino-Soviet talks to be held in Geneva . . . .
> In Isla Vista, California, there are conflicting reports of student violence in that seaside community. The governor of California has mobilized the California National Guard to patrol the Santa Barbara area. Two sheriff's deputies reportedly have been injured by flying bottles or rocks . . . .
> In New York, the Secretary General of the U.N. has called on the United States, the People's Republic of China and the Soviet Union to cease at once their boycott of the Security Council. The Council is meeting in special session because of the threat of war on the Thai border—

He began playing with the dial. She pressed her lips together, waiting until he found some chamber music before speaking. "What *about* the U.N.?"

He sat again and rocked a little. "The President believes that if we go back to the U.N. before I've had an opportunity to talk to them both, then we've lost our leverage."

"Lev-er-age," she repeated, as if it were one of those arcane words that she had been teasing him with. "Leverage. Curious how different administrations use different buzz words. It was 'escalation' in the Johnson years, and that hideous 'linkage' with a German accent—oh, sorry—during the Nixon reign, but yours has always been 'leverage,' hasn't it?" He looked at her, without any comment beyond the brightness in his eyes. She pushed both hands through her hair, then sat with her elbows on the desk, her face pulled taut from the pressure. Her voice was thick with the effort to mute the passion. The string quartet sawed away on her nerves.

"I mean, good God, Wolf. Leverage is based on trust—or credibility, to use *that* meaningless official word. The best leverage you could possibly have is to announce on Monday that you are prepared to go to the U.N. to begin trilateral nuclear disarmament talks with both China and the USSR. How else can you expect to shake the Soviets?"

"Spoken like a true Russell. Look, give me a chance. You're going to China, and not in the press pool—we can say that you're still taking my oral history." She turned to glare at him and he leaned almost into her face. "Listen, don't quote Bertrand Russell to me because you know as well as I do what he said in 1945. He advocated a first strike against the Soviet Union. A 'preventive' atomic strike."

"That was before I was born."

"You devil," he hissed and made her laugh, then held her wrists when she tried to stop her ears. She let her arms go limp so that as he talked he held her hands, moving his rocker so close that their knees touched. She gazed at the configuration of the four hands as they lay two on each thigh, and smiled sadly. Suddenly, she no longer wanted to continue fencing or matching wits with this serious and sensitive man. She felt the need to let down her guard and just talk, for once.

Years later, she began, the old man had told her the complete story. "Just the two of us sitting in the cozy sitting room at Plas Penrhyn in Wales, far enough away from London to avoid some of the expected radioactive fallout from the World War III he knew must come."

This had been in 1966, her first stay with him, in May, and she had held his arm as he appeared at a public celebration of his ninety-fifth birthday. Friends, young and old, sat or stood around the town green looking at a spray of red roses in the center. Next to the flowers was a large, elegant sheet of parchment, spread on the grass, studded with flowers, announcing birthday greetings from a list of well-wishers that included "Plato," "Shakespeare" and everyone of any quality in between. She helped the white-haired Third Earl Russell up the stone steps and out onto the lawn, at which point cheers for "Bertie" rang out.

He had been tired afterwards and requested that he be allowed to take his tea "alone with B.J." (They had decided that it would be better all around if she was referred to as B.J., an Oxford student —true enough—rather than "my granddaughter, illegitimate twice over, and thereby hangs a tale." "Besides," he added, "I *want* history to speculate about why a blooming and one day great beauty began to meet in private with me in my ninety-fourth year." Then they would both chortle and smile into each other's eyes and sip soup or tea. She had almost cried when he told her how he despised the term "illegitimate," and called her, instead, a "love child." Even then, as an adolescent, she had known that she would always be defined by this indomitable man, that she had found her roots in this rocky corner of Wales.

With pipe and cup to brace him, B.R. had told her about his last great crusade. How he had taken a succession of positions after Hiroshima and Nagasaki, the first being that "America use the temporary superiority to insist upon disarmament." By '46 he had said privately that if only "America would war on Russia" that might save the human race, whose prospects were now "somber beyond precedent." Told her sadly how he had thought that a pretext or *casus belli* could be found and the USSR broken before Stalin could develop a nuclear capability. Confessed to her that, "I had always been allergic to the style of Russian life since my first visit in the '20s," and so believed that "another world war was preferable to Russian dominance, especially if that war led to true world government."

Then the old battler had assured her puzzled, blue, sixteen-year-old eyes that he had shifted back and forth on the agonizing question of how to prevent atomic war until 1948. "After '48, there was no choice. The Russians had the bomb too—it was inevitable, nobody had to steal it for them—and either there would be disarmament or extinction. So I gave up blackmailing the Russians and began the Einstein correspondence.

"Einstein on the day of his death wrote to me that his name should be used to petition for disarmament—'There is no defense in science against the weapons that can destroy civilization' . . . A remarkable man, B.J., and so human. His wife once showed me a scrap of doggerel that he had jotted down—

> I shan't be absent, little
> Snookie,
> Though I am not a sugar
> cookie,
> What life has brought you up
> to now
> May sweeten the farewell somehow.

"I miss his presence very much . . ."

For a moment the great philosopher simply stared into her eyes in an unspoken expression of loss as she tried to smile through her tears. She would never forget that moment, that sudden silence broken by the song of the May robins . . . Then he knocked the cold pipe on the round brass tray and roused himself.

"Now with the Americans in Vietnam threatening the whole world, I know that my former position must seem insane to you, but try to remember, B.J., that by 1945 I *had* become a madman obsessed with survival. Not *peace,* but survival. I didn't yet understand that peace was not a goal but a method . . . So, my beautiful B.J., someday you must tell the world that your old B.R. was not a solemn stained-glass saint. I existed for my own center, many things that I did were regrettable. I liked and practiced hypocrisy because if I had not, I should not have been allowed to do my work; but there is no need to continue the hypocrisy after my death. I hated hypocrisy and lies: I loved life and real people, and worked to get rid of the sham that prevents me from loving real people as they really are . . . ."

Only when tears began to fall on their entangled hands did she or Wolf realize that her downcast eyes were weeping. As if in slow motion, he came out of the rocker to kneel at her side. "I'm so sorry, Betsy—"

She took him aback with a wide smile, almost a grin, "No, no, no. You simply reminded me of the first real meeting I ever had with B.R. in Wales, on his birthday. Brought it back to me . . . I did adore him so. I love to remember him even though it always makes me laugh or cry—usually both. But, yes, from '45 to '48 he advocated an ultimatum to the Soviets. After '48 he believed that was insane, and that after '48 American foreign policy was crazy."

"Can any man ever measure up to Russell for you? You've made a brilliant career out of interviewing the so-called great men of the world. Do any of them compare with him?" She shook her head slowly. "Thank God I'm not a great man," he said.

"You're not?"

"Of course not. I'm an adviser to great men. I'm just a *man.*" He lifted his head to look at her. She watched as his eyes fell to her breasts beneath the vest and the Cacharel-print shirt.

She talked as she began to unbutton her shirt. The string quartet was now into Mozart, she was glad for that. Because the room was well lit and their faces were no more than a foot apart, and because their faces and hands were the only naked surfaces of their bodies, they could see in each other's eyes and features the subtle but profound transitions and changes as the sexual hunger grew. She paused after the first button as if to allow some little time for their critical faculties to close the gap on their racing desires. The Mozart seemed to have hypnotized him, she noticed; his eyes were enlarged and blue as a boy's.

She continued huskily, at the level of political abstraction, though she saw that his crotch was bulging just as he could see her nipples go hard and erect under her shirt. Her breathing only allowed her to phrase three or four words at a time. Her eyes appeared fixed on his as she tried to maintain her control. It was, of course, a losing battle.

"Not a 'great man'?" She tried unsuccessfully to smile. "Just a man? What splendid nonsense. You can't even keep a straight face. Why you're an 'action intellectual,' ah, the brightest and the best, the *power* intellectual who plays a more important role in American politics than any priest or shaman or wise man in the history of power—the manager of the empire, the lone gun, the master of . . ."

Her breathing overwhelmed the soliloquy. They both looked at his fingers trembling on her knee. Her fingers fell to the next button and fumbled for purchase there while his fingers, in sympathy, moved searchingly on her left knee and lower thigh. The Mozart played in the clear for a moment, then he began to talk. The sense of their words had now sunk below the meaning of their voices. His fingers swam through the air as through water toward her third and last button as he spoke.

"Just a man, an expert if you like, who, uh, helps the 'great men' with the, huh, nuts and bolts; teaches these principled saints and heroes how to compromise . . . Shaw said something about, uh, when I think of my own unfortunate character, smirched with compromise, rotted with opportunism, mildewed by experience . . . who are they to, ah . . ."

At last the shirt hung open and her breasts stood free: the aureoles a suffused dark pink, each nipple thrusting its swelling flesh toward him. The wit died on his dry lips and his eyes widened, sparkled. In the silence, there was their breathing and the Mozart. She gave unspoken thanks that the deadly and routine roar of the helicopter was absent for once. She watched his eyes watching her, she could sense, almost see her breasts reflected in his enlarged pupils. His fingers had fallen away from her blouse, now both hands rose again to touch her, the arched palms cupping her fullness with a gentle pressure. She was breathing through her mouth, head back, skewered by an overmastering need for him . . . "I suppose it's inevitable that at a moment of historical crisis that there should be popular and carnal revolt, oh God, I want you now—"

"Listen," he breathed, "I keep a sort of safe suite on the sixth floor. It's better to go there."

"No bugs?"

"No bugs—to speak of."

"All right, let's go before I rape you right here before God, the CIA and your SS." But they could not manage laughter as they rose, because both their knees and their lips were trembling with their desire.

5

WASHINGTON, D.C.—JANUARY 14, 1984 (SATURDAY NIGHT)

There were two white plastic toothbrushes in the bathroom of the "safe suite." Even as she undressed, her reportorial eye continued to gather information on Wolf Manheim. The bathroom, like the rest of the small suite, was bare and clinical. The perfect anonymity of the place intensified, somehow, the somehow existential nakedness of their encounter. The tile between the bath mat and the bedroom carpet was cold on her bare feet as she stepped into the room and then leaned back to switch off the bathroom overhead light.

The dim illumination in the bedroom came from the foyer. There was no console and so no music, no sound except the distant and irregular visits of the official helicopters. There were no books, no paintings on the white walls, nothing except Wolf Manheim lying there naked and waiting under a sheet on the narrow single bed. He rose on one elbow to watch her as she slowly approached, giving himself time to look at her. Again she saw herself as he was seeing her—her long, contoured legs and thrusting breasts, the curve of her neck as it flowed down into the collarbones highlighted against her skin. The arch and curve—hip, buttock and thigh—and the spilled honey hair growing up halfway to her navel . . . he wanted to see all of her. His eyes were glistening, dwelling on her thighs. She knew that he wanted her to turn around, so she modeled for him, hip and thigh and high buttock, then she laughed softly, "Are you ready to be raped?" She threw herself balletically onto the bed next to him and leaned on one arm also. "What if this were the last time you could ever make love? That wakes you up, my dear boy, doesn't it? I mean about making war, not love." Absently, she stroked his smooth, muscled chest, pushing the sheet down past the navel before stopping. "Jesus."

She couldn't help thinking that Wolf Manheim's cock was like himself—long, corded, big-headed. "Priapus," she smiled, her breathing upset again as he gently pinched one of her nipples between his fingers. "Wait," she said.

She had to stretch to reach her tote bag from the edge of the bed. She dragged the old suede world traveler over and fished out her diaphragm container. It would be a sacrilege to have to sheathe that olympic specimen. She lay on her back, drew her legs up and rested the paraphernalia on the curve of her abdomen. Wolf was sitting up, taken aback, she sensed, for once. He was wide-eyed, watching her handle the smooth-surfaced disposable applicator. The three-inch white plastic unit seemed to gather the existing light so that it almost glowed in her hand. She slowly exerted pressure with her fingertips, causing a pearly cream to flow out into the center of the diaphragm. Expertly, with her little finger, she spread the spermacide around the rim and dropped the exhausted applicator to the floor. Finally, she folded the diaphragm and pushed it slowly into her vagina as, at the same time, she drew her long legs up and back.

"Remarkable," he said at last. "All this on the last night before the end of the world?"

"In case I'm one of the ten percent that survive. Two generations of bastards are enough. Here—"

"What about me?"

"Oh, no," she chuckled, "great men and their hired guns go first. Here." She rubbed the excess cream from her palms and fingers into a thin consistency and then transferred the moisture onto his penis with a slow, rolling motion. He sank back with a sigh. Her hand slipped down to massage his aching testicles, explore his thighs, and gingerly tip one finger into his anus. "No?"

"No, just like that."

With one hand he joined her in rubbing the shaft, while with his right hand he reached between her legs, where she crouched over him. She arched with pleasure as he eased two fingers in, then slid her torso, as if in a dance, down on him and began to tongue his cock, up and down, slowly. When she put her soft lips over the head, he groaned and arched. "Don't come yet, please," she whispered. "No," he answered, full voice, stroking her head and neck, touching her ears with his fingertips.

As she moved, sucking him, his long arm followed her as she circled him until she was at his knees and out of reach, then he saw that she was touching her own clitoris as she continued to draw him deeper and deeper into her mouth. His reflexes were driving the head and shaft of his erection back into her throat. Her hips and buttocks were elevated as she descended on him, and rotating, too. Calling, "I can't wait," bending over him, sinking down on the powerful flesh and bone, she saw that he had been watching her. She rose up on him, his hips came up to meet her, and his hands shot up to lift her breasts. Then she called out, "Come with me!"

Minutes later, she rose from his chest and realized that he had not come, that he was like a ramrod inside her; she could feel his pulse. "Is this true?" she asked, and began pumping and twisting, riding high until she cried out again.

When her thighs had begun to tremble and she could no longer remain on top, he rolled her over in one slow motion, still deep inside her. He sank his fingers into her firm buttock. She watched him look down on her from his height, while her breasts and belly flamed with residual heat. The multiple orgasms had left her legs trembling; he had to grip her buttocks so hard that she could feel the cutting pressure of his dull fingernails. For the first time in her life she was afraid she would pass out. And still he did not explode, rocking her now with such force that she had to grab the brass spokes of the headboard and push to keep from being driven into it. The room swam as he pulled her out and up to meet each pounding thrust. Again, over and over again, until he flung back his distended neck—"Ahh . . ." His coming lifted her literally off the bed, hips first so that her head and hair hung down as if her neck had been snapped. Her hands sought blindly and found the whipcords of his chest and neck. He held her that way in a frieze, nothing moving except his pelvis as his seed shot and spasmed into her.

WASHINGTON, D.C.—JANUARY 15, 1984
(SUNDAY MORNING)

"It's ten o'clock," she said, walking very slowly back to the bed. "How did you sleep?"

"Sleep? I died and went to heaven and am reborn and suddenly do not at all want the world to end. Can you fix it up for me? Oh, I'm *sore*. Are you some kind of god, or merely afflicted with the most stylish case of priapasitus on record?"

His craggy face broke down into a full-fledged grin. She sank beside him and sighed deeply. He reached over to hold her hip, then inched an exploratory finger to the lips of her vulva. "Not until after you've kept your promise to tell me about how you pulled off the great Shah caper. Come on. I presume that inasmuch as you're here, nobody has declared war on anybody yet?"

"Probably not." He detoured his hand to merely stroke her smooth flank.

"Balls," she said, "you know damn well that nothing is going to

67

happen before you talk to the Chinese and the Russians. Isn't that right, Dr. Strangelove?" His riposte was to cup her pelvis hard. "Oww! I'm sore, I told you. All right, you tell about the Shah and I'll shut up."

"Done. And then you'll tell me more about B.R. and then I'm going to give you a dog of the hair that bit you to make you feel better, and then we're going to Chester's for steak and eggs."

"We'll see, we'll see."

So he told her, very much off the record, about how he had become the secret man of the hour in 1979, never again quite able to leave center stage. All the while tracing the curves of her belly and breasts, up to the highlights of her collarbones and around and down again. "Lovely," she murmured from time to time, in appreciation of his touch as well as the story of the Shah, which she told him was "tickling my fancy."

She laughed out loud when he described the luxurious sick-bay setup for the deposed monarch on the enclosed fourteenth floor of New York Hospital—"Three television sets, a telex, a WATS line, a giant wine cooler, and a harem of beds and cubicles for family and staff."

"I love it, I love it," Betsy said. "Tell me where he kept the Great Danes and poodles. You see, I know more than you think." He paid no attention to her interjections, just kept stroking her legs and talking.

"The President was beside himself because, as you know, from the start he had been against the Kissinger people's plea to sneak the Shah *into* the U.S. And then the embassy in Teheran had warned him. So he told the hawks—

"Wait," she murmured.

"—then I started shuttling between New York and Lackland to get the big banker to convince the Shah that Panama was a Paradise on earth . . ."

She sat up happily. "So you convinced him to make a few loans to patriots in Panama and to give Mohammed Riza Pahlavi his marching orders. And with this master stroke and a convenient leak to a network news anchor about the 'secret shuttle,' you were made forever! And in the nick of time."

He lay back and stretched. "It could have been World War III, all right, and unlike today the country would have been one hundred percent behind us."

"That I doubt . . . And so there were no Soviet KGB agents involved in the takeover of the embassy in Iran, were there?"

"We never found out," he said.

"Um. What else did they have on you, I mean on the U.S.?"

"Oh, you know, links between SAVAK and other intelligence services."

"The CIA."

He pretended to doze off.

"And South Africa?"

Silence.

"Wake up—and Rhodesia and Britain and—"

"Betsy, stop, you're insatiable.

"But, Wolf, that was such a crazy period and it's never been properly sorted out. What no one can understand to this day is why the hardliners, why CIA, supported *you*—"

"They supported me because they did not *want* a war starting in the Middle East."

"Why not?"

"Probably because they felt we weren't ready . . . Anyway, that's why they had to have a so-called dove and not a true-believing hawk next to a president who had sunk again to a sub-Nixon popularity—"

"Listen, Wolf—"

"B.J., no more . . . stop it, that tickles, stop it . . . No, ahh, ahh. Oh, yes, that's—"

"Shh, shh, Wolf—I promise I'll stop after this—*why* did Kissinger risk so much to get the Shah to New York? And then Carter leaping in after him?"

"He *owed* the Shah. And *we,* the Administration, owed *him*—they were convinced that without Kissinger there would have been neither a Panama Canal nor a SALT II Treaty. I disagreed, and I warned them that the Shah could blow up in our face."

They lay there in quiet; only one of the official helicopters could be heard. A dull winter light washed over the bare room. His hand worked its way back to play in her pubic hair. She reached over to measure the girth of his cock at rest. "I knew Henry, too," she said. "Some say that he couldn't get it up . . . and you can't get it *down* —but don't misunderstand me, I believe there is a substantive difference in the two conditions."

"Who's 'some'?"

"When we had our 'date' all he did was talk about himself, while the Secret Service were crawling around in the bushes (by the way, how did you get rid of Spiderman—what's his name? Jim and the boys, they're not watching us on closed circuit at this very moment, are they?)." She could feel him laughing quietly into her neck. "I'm not shocked about the Shah's adventures in this country. Men or women, these Oriental despots seem to like it only one way, back door, I believe it's called. Especially what the old shahs referred to as 'unbearded slave boys.' Women were so much meat to the Shah's court—and *he* took credit for liberating women, that *is* rich!"

He had slipped his hand down to touch the lips and she felt the base of his shaft begin to thicken again.

He had two fingers in her vagina now, she was wet and he massaged her anus, probing. "They're meat to them," she said again. "Before they kill them, the SAVAK sodomize them. The Shah did it to the whole country—"

She was too short of breath to continue. He was turning her over and positioning her hips. He was over her; with her face turned profile on the pillow she could see him out of the corner of her eye as he bent low. Then she closed her eyes, giving little cries as she felt his tongue grooving her, back and forth, orifice to orifice. Her eyes shot open when his erection made its entrance. Wet as she was and lubricated by desire, his penetration took her breath away, but he was gentle, slow, and sensitive to her.

Her face was flushed, red welts of passion covered her body. With her remaining strength she lifted her head and looked back to see. He held her hips high, slowly he was working himself deeper and deeper. The muscles of his throat, chest and arms were standing out. He glistened with sweat. His head went back. She reached up to hold her pumping clitoris as he began to ride her . . .

She was awakened by a violent reaction from Wolf. By the time she could turn over and sit up, the gunman had positioned himself in the bathroom doorway, just to the right of the entrance to the bedroom. He held the Luger with silencer leveled at the National Security Adviser, barely looking at her.

She studied him. He looked about thirty, medium height, slim, and eyes full of tears behind large glasses. For a moment she thought he was going to shoot Wolf or both of them on the spot, but then he unbuttoned the thick blue peacoat and eased off the knit stocking cap. "Get dressed, Manheim, very slowly, and don't do anything heroic. You know that if I was able to find your little hideaway here that I have backup outside to take care of you and any of your people." She tried to catch the slight accent.

Wolf was positioned in front of the sliding doors of the closet, naked, dwarfing the gunman. "There are no guards in the corridor," Wolf said evenly, "so you could be alone."

"Then I suggest you try something, you *degenerado.*" Wolf froze. Was he Cuban? He looked to Betsy like any long-brown-haired graduate student from George Washington or Catholic University. He was nervous and his voice shook, but he would use the gun, she believed and, obviously, so did the National Security Adviser, especially if the man was acting alone. Wolf began to dress slowly, taking time, keeping his voice measured. "Can you tell me what this is about?"

The gunman spoke levelly to her, calling her by name. "Ms. Russell, despite what I see before my eyes, I believe that you are the same woman who has been the single voice of honest criticism in the media over the last few years, and who has called the junta in Chile butchers and stooges. Therefore, we believe that you will deliver our message to the media and act as a representative of any negotiating that is set up. Am I right?"

So he was Chilean. Wolf Manheim had been an aide of the National Security Advisor from 1969 to 1973, until the overthrow of the elected government in Santiago. Only after the coup, she remembered, had Wolf left the Nixon administration. She realized that the young terrorist was scandalized at finding her naked in bed with Manheim.

"Put the tape recorder on, please . . . and *you* keep on dressing, warm clothes, then sit down on the floor, away from the bed . . . don't say anything, not a word . . . Turn the tape on, Ms. Russell. We ask that after you give the story to the London *Times* you make copies of the tape generally available. Thank you."

She covered herself with the sheet as she reached for the recorder. In rapid Spanish, most of which she could understand, the youth identified himself as a member of the *Acción Revolucionario* (AR), and Wolfgang Manheim as an international criminal who, together with Henry Kissinger and others, was guilty "of crimes against humanity in the sense of the Nuremberg Tribunals." He never took the Luger off of his target but spoke in a high, clear voice, so that the tape would pick him up.

"El Doctor Manheim sera detenido por la Acción Revolucionaria hasta (1) que la junta fascista en Santiago libre un grupo de detenidos politicas, cuyos nombres serán dados al diario El London Times . . ."

"Dr. Manheim will be detained by the AR until (1) the illegal junta in Santiago releases a group of political prisoners here listed and delivered to the London *Times;* (2) a ransom of ten million dollars is delivered to our intermediary by the government of the United States; and (3) that the documents for the U.S. CIA operation 'Quartered Man' be released to the media in their entirety."

" . . . You can turn it off now," he said in English and took a step as if ready to leave with his prisoner.

"What is the Quartered Man . . . *El Descuartizado?*" Her question made him pause. She was sitting now on the bed, covered below the waist, and she pulled the sheet up to cover her breasts.

"You tell her what the 'Quartered Man' was, Dr. Manheim. After all, you're one of the authors, aren't you?"

"*El Descuartizado?* What—"

"*El Descuartizado,* yes, and CAMELOT and CENTAUR and TRACKS I and II and PLAN SEPTEMBER and all the other operations against my country hatched by you and the others in your '40 Committee' and the Psychological Warfare Division of the CIA."

The eyes behind the glasses burned toward Wolf, who, she saw, had flushed a dull pink. "No," he kept the gun on Wolf, "that minor chapter in the glorious history of the United States has slipped his steel trap of a mind. After all, it all began so long ago, way back in the '60s when Dr. Manheim was a Peace Corps executive in Chile trying to win hearts and minds. But *I'll* tell you. *You* stay sitting right there where you are until I tell you to move." He spoke almost accentless English. He must be a Chilean-American, she thought.

"I know about CAMELOT"—she started to say, hoping to draw him out, somehow talk him out of it.

"Of course," he nodded, "their cover was blown in 1964 when the young Dr. Manheim and his idealistic college kids and grandmothers found out that the 'sociological study' they were making, all across Chile, was intended to tell the Pentagon how each class of Chileans would react or not react to the imposition of a military government." He raced ahead in English and Spanish, telling the story of how CAMELOT's statistics had paved the way for bought elections, corrupted generals, and staged violence through TRACKS I and II. As he talked the young Chilean gesticulated with the gun. He's not part of a team, she thought, he's not under discipline.

"But," the young revolutionary's voice was a cutting wire of outrage, "the 'Quartered Man' campaign was the climax. *El Descuartizado* was the name the CIA press gave to a crime that left the torso of a murdered man at the National Soccer Stadium. We know now that the CIA kept the crime alive for two years in *El Mercurio* and their other controlled media until after the coup in 1973. There were scare headlines—'WIFE OF QUARTERED MAN DISAPPEARS,' and 'QUARTERED MAN BELIEVED BEHIND DEATH OF WIFE'S LOVER,' and 'HOUSEWIFE BUYS SAUSAGES OF HUMAN FLESH,' and so on and on, always working in references to leftists who raped and cannibalized. Then came your lies of how the left-wing government was plotting to *descabezar* the military—but the word means *both* 'retire' and *'decapitate'* in Spanish. Then we . . ."

The gunman was trembling, the Luger shaking dangerously.

". . . and more headlines and forged letters to the military officers, from the 'Reds,' naming their children's names who would *also* be beheaded. And more human sausages, and *'El Descuartizado Vive!'* as coup day dawned, and the mummies, *las momias,* the rich women in tight pants and furs beating their pots and pans in front of the Palace, night and day—"

He was screaming at her now, forgetting to watch his hostage— "until Chile was driven mad and the troops poured out of their barracks shouting for blood—and the torture began and it has never stopped! They set up torture and concentration camps, *Chile became a concentration camp.* They wired up our genitals, they broke our fingers, they drowned us, we froze to death in the Strait of Magellan." She could just see Wolf beginning to hunch forward off the floor—"We were scalded and raped and whipped *and quartered* —We were the Quartered Men! Chile was the—"

Manheim seemed to rocket off the floor. She could hear the youth's ribs crack as he went down under Wolf's flying lunge. The pistol bounced off her tape recorder onto the carpet. Before she could reach for the gun, she heard a crunch and looked up to see that Wolf had driven his leg and knee into the youth's head with such force that the skull had been smashed halfway into the white plaster wall.

"You've *killed* him." But Wolf could not answer, his seizure had begun.

7

BUCHENWALD—JANUARY 27, 1944

After two weeks in the camp, Dr. Manheim told the boy that he must assist Father Thyle in the preparation of "Special Autopsies." Meticulous documents were required by Berlin and the boy had a clear hand, with a talent for organizing documents quite beyond his years.

He liked Father Thyle, a Catholic monk from Poland kept alive by senior inmate Doctor Manheim. He was small and humped, with a sharp face and huge, beautiful blue eyes. The SS hated to look at him, and so he rarely left his "office." The doctor told the boy that there was "a daily beauty in Father Thyle's life that makes *them* ugly." The sturdy inmate leader planted himself in front of the boy and stared down at the long, aristocratic face, saying, "Try not to look like a saint or a martyr, teach yourself to look like other men, ordinary men." He brushed the fine hair off the boy's forehead. "Go with Father Thyle and trust him absolutely, he is an innocent child and a very deep teacher at the same time. He is a great man, surely the greatest in this camp, so you must listen to him, and learn . . . But do *not* follow him."

77

For the first few days the monk instructed the boy in how to fill in the various forms that each corpse generated in "Special Autopsy." Their office was located between the hospital and the "Bunker." At first Wolfgang did not even know what went on in the Bunker. The Special Autopsy office consisted of two rooms, one much larger than the other, lined with filing cases. The monk made weak tea on the stove that their official quarters boasted. It was the only warmth in their area, so the boy kept it stoked.

The typewriter was an Olympia in good repair. Soon Wolfie, as the monk affectionately referred to him, was typing up that prisoner number such and such was— *"admitted to the hospital complaining of chest pain and fever . . . Despite intensive therapy, all efforts to improve the condition of the patient failed . . . Cause of death: cardiac weakness complicated by pneumonia."* Then the boy would write out the Camp Medical Officer's signature just as he had practiced. There were no dead bodies to go with the names and serial numbers. "Another ghost," the monk would say, his sharp features pointing downward like arrows, and make the sign of the cross in the air as if he could see the deceased in the smoke curling up from the little stove.

The little Father handled each form not as if it were an abstraction but a thing living, each name seemed to have dimension for him. He would say to the boy, "Wolfie, these are souls, each one, that you are typing up. Yes, well, what about the souls of the others, the pastor's and farmer's sons, the SS, who have slaughtered these innocents? Are these two races of men? In nature we know that the answer is no. Did God, then, create devils and men to cohabit like victim and executioner in the selfsame prison cell? That cannot be the case either, since there would then be nothing but unequal suffering in the world, and we know that that is not true because in love of children and all that's innocent we feel ineffable joy and not just pain. Why? . . . Why not? When we rub shoulders we overcome our miserable separate personalities, we do not live just for ourselves alone, and at those moments, Wolfie, we catch a glimpse of what we are *intended* to be . . . We have come so far, you know, from plants to animals to apes to you and me. Wolfie, we are the creatures that have been called men too soon."

As if dancing, the hunchback would skip up to the boy to stroke his forehead, then drop to his knees in front of him, then leap up as if on fire to dance again—and all the while talking in a soft, furry voice, it seemed to the boy—without pause, except to cough. Transfigured—the little monk falling at the boy's feet, where he huddled near the stove, or rising to dance out his stations of the cross in the cramped office. Chanting, *"Bogu potrzebny jest Czlowiek,* God needs man, God needs man! *A co jezeli Czlowiek nie jest calkowicie potworny?* And what if man is not altogether monstrous?" Then his blue eyes would shine and he would laugh silently and so would the boy.

"It is not for us to judge the Nazis *or* to forgive them—or ourselves. We are not God nor the devil. It is up to us to keep men from putting themselves in such a situation because then we all become actors in these crimes. It is our calling to warn men that the worst can happen and will happen, that it has *already* happened, that there *is* judgment day and no matter what crimes we have committed or contemplated, it is not too late to save ourselves. Because of their guilt this drives them wild because they *know* that it is not too late—so that is why we whisper in their ear the little question, the only question: 'What if man is not altogether monstrous?' "

And the boy would write and fill in the blanks:

Dear Mrs. _____
 Your husband, _____, died in the Camp
Hospital on _____ . May I express my sincere sympathy on your bereavement.
 _____was admitted to the hospital on _____

with severe symptoms of exhaustion, complaining of diffi-
culty in breathing and of pains in the chest. Despite compe-
tent medication and devoted medical attention it proved
impossible, unfortunately, to keep the patient alive.

The deceased voiced no final requests.

The Camp Commandant

And sign the Commandant's name, Karl Koch. The boy had not
yet learned that the Commandant's plump wife, Ilse, had prisoners
making lampshades from the skins of some of the men whose names
the boy was filling in on letters to loved ones at home.

Then one day the monk sat next to the boy and gave him tea.
"Your father is afraid that this time he cannot keep them from
sending me to Auschwitz. The fools, can't they see that I'm dying
right here?" He coughed silently and it was true, the boy could see
that the monk's skin was yellow with jaundice and his eyes were red.
"But so many of these SS are the sons of pastors and because I preach
Jesus Christ risen it reminds them of their childhood beliefs . . . You
are a Jewish boy, do you believe in the coming of the Messiah?" He
coughed soundlessly, while the boy fetched him a glass of tea, not
bothering to say that he was a Communist and not a Jew. The monk
whispered in Hebrew "*Adonai Tsarich* . . .

"Dr. Manheim is Communist, but you are so innocent and young
that I do not know if you will be able to stand it without the hope
of the Messiah . . ." Wolfgang did not know what to answer but
only stared at the yellow and dying little man trying to warm his
shivering hands around the tea glass. The day before the monk had
been warned that the Communist *kapo* infrastructure which ran the
bureaucracy of the camp could no longer postpone the priest's
transfer, so he decided to initiate the boy into the secrets of the
"Bunker."

The Bunker adjoined the empty "stables." The monk took him
there first. "Wolfie, may God forgive me, *Boze zmiluj sie nad nami,*

that I must be the one to tell you about where the names in our files and ledgers come from. But someone must live to tell their stories, the lies that we mail to families must someday be confessed. We should have, if we could have, written a separate letter describing each single death—but that could not be, yet." He was not much taller, any longer, than the boy as his silent coughing seemed to pull him in and down upon himself. The two small figures stepped into the cold stable that smelled like straw and something else—what? —to the boy.

"Here the truck backs in with the prisoners. Immediately, here, they are ordered to undress. The valuables and dog tags go on this table here to be carefully noted. Then through here to the 'Medical Room,' here the SS doctors—" The monk broke off in a paroxysm of coughing so complete that he had to lean on the boy. The effort forced tears to run down into the darkened hollows of his yellow cheeks. When his breath returned, he exhaled, "My God, my God," turning away from the table covered with shining medical cutting instruments toward a small room on their left. His voice was a thin rasp now, no longer soft, and his beautiful pale blue eyes had turned almost white.

"This is the SS shooting room. They stand on this little rise behind this partition and stick their guns through this opening. Another SS man stands behind this screen with a hose and, may God forgive me, this curtain covers the wall, see here behind it are the bullet holes.

"Out here are the spaces for storing straw and sawdust. May God have mercy on me, the bodies are piled here and this drainpipe carries away the blood to fertilize the vegetable patch that we walked through. Then another truck waits here to carry the bodies away. Then, at last, the names and papers are sent over to us for 'Special Autopsy.' May God forgive us."

The boy could not stop himself from blurting out—"But where is God, Father?"

The monk's breathing was shallow and his lips were moist. "He will come, when man comes. Not before."

So they passed out of the "stable" to the Bunker. First the boy was shown the "dog cells", where the prisoners were forced to lie huddled on one side and bark for their food. The monk hurried him past the interrogation cells where Master Sergeant Sommer tortured and tore men apart, sometimes with his bare hands, all under the control of the camp "Political Department." The boy took passing note out of the corner of his eye of the truncheons and whips hanging along the dark, narrow hall.

The document ordering these atrocities always read "The prisoner is to be examined until he confesses." Then Sommer would immerse the testicles of his subjects in freezing and boiling water, by turns, followed by an iodine painting that tore off the skin in strips. If the inmate was a "difficult case," he would be throttled, starved, suspended from ropes by the arms and then by the legs. In the end, each was given a cup of drugged tea and then the SS would inject a fatal dose of poison. The official form filled out by the little monk and the boy always read, "Death by circulatory failure."

While the prisoners waited for their torture, they were not allowed to sleep or pace their cells, but, the priest told Wolfgang, they must stand at absolute attention from five in the morning until ten at night. The peephole in the cell door was a magnifying lens that allowed Sommer and the guards to note the smallest infraction of "rules." Any movement from within brought twenty-five lashes and the offender had then to immerse his head in the excrement-filled toilet bowl. Only later did the boy find out that on occasion Sommer and the SS would herd prisoners into the corridor and kick and trample them to death with their boots. Again, any inmate who "stared shamelessly" at the Commandant's wife, Frau Koch, would have his serial number noted down by that Junoesque lady and a day later would find himself being given a fatal injection, in the Bunker, of air or chloral hydrate.

All this the boy learned that day, and more later. The drunken-
ness of the guards; the martyrdom of those tortured, sometimes for
a year at a time; those who, still alive in the truck transporting
bodies, called out—"Give me your hand, friend, in the name of
God!" Or, sometimes, a prisoner would shriek, "We today, you
tomorrow!" And once an Italian dancer forced to perform naked
had managed to seize an SS officer's gun and kill him before she,
herself, was riddled with bullets.

All this and more the boy saw and heard.

On the day that the little monk disappeared, Dr. Manheim told
the boy, "Don't cry, Wolfie, the Father was not 'selected' for
Auschwitz after all. He . . . he forced Sommer to kill him on the
spot, last night. He went into the SS day room and found Sommer
alone. He had already told some of us what he intended to say.
'What do you want, dwarf?' Sommer screamed at him. 'To tell you
personally that Jesus Christ is risen and coming,' said Father Thyle,
'and that you must *not* be afraid to change your thoughts!' And that
was the end of it. Never mind, I will fill out the official autopsy
report for you . . . You lie down in the ward room and rest
now . . ."

January 13, 1984, London Times

FALSE NUCLEAR ALERTS
CONCERN PENTAGON

BETSY JONES-RUSSELL

WASHINGTON—While National Security Adviser Wolf Manheim has played down the significance of the two false nuclear alerts last week, officials report that the incidents have stirred deep concern within the Defense Department and the White House.

At the Pentagon officials disclosed that Gen. Victor T. Kramer yesterday secretly visited the headquarters of the Strategic Air Command in Omaha, Neb., to confer with senior officers there on the false alarms. Today, Kramer is scheduled to visit the Air Force's underground complex at Cheyenne Mountain, Colo., the site of the North American Air Defense Command.

Tass, the official Soviet news agency, responding to Tuesday's false alarm, said Saturday that the computer malfunction meant "during several minutes the world was on the brink of a nuclear war."

Dr. Manheim was described by a close aide as being "very upset" about the incidents.

Administration critics are comparing the recent malfunctions to a series of false alarms several years ago. According to Pentagon sources, a new set of "fail-safe" human oversight procedures were instituted in 1981 to avoid a repetition of the alarming accidents. When queried whether last week's close call was attributable to technological failure or to inadequate command and control procedures, the National Security Adviser refused to comment.

85

Experts say it would currently take about nine minutes for missiles launched by Russian submarines to strike American bomber bases and a half hour for ICBMs fired from inside the Soviet Union to hit targets in the United States. For this reason, according to certain White House officials, although under existing law the President alone has the base authority to order the release of nuclear weapons, this authority . . . *may* be delegated to subordinate officers in the chain of command.

8

AIR FORCE TWO TO CHINA— JANUARY 19, 1984
(THURSDAY)

BETSY JONES-RUSSELL: Testing . . . Testing one, two . . . Right. Manheim tape three, side one. Thursday, 19th January, 1984. 10:14 A.M. aboard *Air Force Two*, en route Beijing via Honolulu . . . Testing, one, two, three, four—dammit—one, two, three . . . There we are . . . Dr. Manheim, in his speech to the nation on Tuesday night, the President stated that, quote, "in the event of war between the People's Republic of China and the Soviet Union, the United States would take immediate steps in its own self-interest," close quotes. This statement and others this week—many of them attributed to you—have led the French and others to charge the U.S. with further undermining the international situation. What *is* the meaning of these veiled threats?

WOLFGANG MANHEIM: I don't think that they are "veiled," Ms. Russell. . . . Here, Peter, please route this through Mac to the President and ask Jim to send us a continental breakfast in here,

87

and then leave us alone for an hour or so. Thanks, Peter . . . Now. We have mutual defense treaty arrangements with China and Thailand; the Soviets, of course, are backing their client Vietnam. The Soviets must know that if Vietnamese troops overrun the Thai border using sophisticated Soviet weapons, and China moves into Vietnam in response and, in turn, the Soviets confront China—

B.J-R: Which is virtually what is happening now.

W.M.: Exactly: We do not want either one to assume that either (A) the United States will *automatically* go to war with Vietnam— much less the Soviet Union—over Thailand; or (B) that because the PRC and the USSR have *both* threatened tactical nuclear weapons that *therefore* the United States has some sort of moral imperative to wash its hands of the matter.

B.J-R: In other words, if Vietnam invades Thailand and China invades Vietnam and the Soviets invade China, and *China*—as threatened—responds with her tactical 80TU-16 bombers and S-022 missiles, supplied by the U.S.—then the government of the United States will do what?

W.M.: Whatever is in our best interests. We would not encourage, even if we could, the PRC to surrender to vastly superior Soviet missile power.

B.J-R: If I'm understanding you, the only way that you might stop a Chinese nuclear response to Soviet ultimatums is to interpose U.S. might *between* PRC and USSR forces, and, thus positioned, use your famous "leverage" to call off World War III.

W.M.: An interesting scenario . . . Ah, here is our breakfast lacking only milk for Ms. Russell's tea, I believe, Jim. Thanks. May we turn this off or would you like to catch me slurping coffee? . . .

"That ferret, Jim, purposely 'forgot' the milk, you know. There's a day's flying to Honolulu and another to Beijing, so *what* is so difficult about our having this cabin to ourselves to continue the interview? I haven't been able to talk to you without interruption since . . ." She lowered her voice. "Tonight, on the beach . . . ?"
He nodded, and they picked at their brioches in silence, both aware that Air Force Two was thoroughly monitored by CIA penetration

agents in the Secret Service and by a range of electronic systems, to say nothing of the women in the typing pool on the other side of the leather accordion doors.

Jim Jarrell reappeared with the milk. Today he wore a Scotch plaid code bar in his lapel, as did all fifty agents on the plane with the delegation. On Sunday she had had it out with Mr. Jarrell. . . .

At first she had thought that when Wolf killed the young Chilean he had somehow injured himself. Then when she bent over the two bodies, she realized that Wolf was probably suffering from an attack of *petit mal.* She partly covered him and hid the Luger away, planning to get rid of it later. Then she took her time washing and dressing, thinking the incredible scene through. When she was certain that her priorities were in order she acted with efficiency, forcing herself first to look at the dead youth. His eyes were open behind broken glasses.

She touched him, he was warm. She had seen B.R. dead and not been frightened. Her mother had been a closed coffin, so that hardly counted . . . She knelt between the two bodies. Wolf's eyes were closed, his breathing shallow and irregular. His long legs twitched momentarily as if he were caught in a bad dream. The blood from the Chilean's head was beginning to congeal on the floor, inches from her knee. The Sunday quiet was complete.

She looked again at the Chilean, his mouth was open slightly now, as if he would speak. Wolf twitched again as if in a trance.

"I am kneeling here between the living and the dead," she mused, "or rather, the dead and the unconscious, like an Egyptian priestess. Shut up!—stop writing poetry!" she told herself and looked up to see if a helicopter was approaching.

She looked down again. The boy's jaw was slack now. There was an acid taste in her mouth. Her knees began to ache. She would have to move to search him. The corpse—that was what he was now, she told herself—was losing color as she watched. Soon he would be cold. She could hear Wolf's breathing. From her angle she could see into the shadowy orifice of the dead man's mouth and throat. "All that pain and twisted love—gone, just like that."

She stripped the man's pockets. No identification. Then she made the bed and checked the corridor. Empty. Then she risked an overseas call to a London physician, a friend, who knew about these implosions of the nervous system called *petit mal.* Within fifteen minutes of the call a key turned in the locked door and Jim Jarrell, ahead of three other agents, came in, all with their service automatics drawn. She knew that she could not afford to lose the initiative so she crossed to the apartment door as the agents fanned out to search the three rooms. "You don't need your weapons," she called in clear tones, "this man blundered in here somehow—because the door had been opened prior to leaving—and he demanded money, and, uh, Dr. Manheim disarmed him and in the process fell and lost consciousness. I have talked to a doctor and he is not to be moved."

The four men in windbreakers and shaded glasses stared at her. Now she could hear two helicopters chopping, could feel the wave of resentment. How far would they go if some random act of violence triggered them? The tableau disolved as Wolf stirred and slowly sat up. His eyes were numb as he focused on the faces. He spoke slowly, working his long jaw as if he had been injected with novocaine for dental surgery. "Jim. Ms. Russell, you've told Mr. Jarrell the facts?" The words were badly slurred; the agents looked at him with some alarm and a touch of disdain for his vulnerability, though it was precisely the vulnerability that stirred her; that this powerful specimen could be struck down from within by "Caesar's sickness" was one of those natural tragedies that seemed to have been visited on great men throughout history. She knew how B.R. had dreaded fits all his life, unnecessarily. She answered softly on cue, "Yes, they know that a robbery attempt was made and that you . . ."

After they had left the body for Jarrell's people to dispose of, in their own way, they had gone up to Wolfe's official suite. He was ashen. They sat by the window staring out at the bleak Sunday. He drank tea with bourbon, honey and lemon. "Thank you very much," he said slowly, weakly. She wanted very much to make some sense of it all with him, but he was obviously still shaken from his attack. She did say, "Wolf, your 'headaches' are serious. I know that, and don't be afraid that I'm going to print it. When you feel better, sometime, you can tell me what you care to."

Slowly he had turned his pale face toward her. "Thank you . . . I have to rest now. Then Camp David tomorrow. Thursday we go to China together.—I *will* talk to you . . . Betsy, I had to kill that boy. He was out of his mind. I wasn't involved in anything called the 'Quartered Man.' I *want* to talk to you."

"I know just the place. On the beach at Waikiki."

"What?" He looked disoriented again.

"On our way to China when we stop for the night in Honolulu. I know just the place." . . .

Now the powerful new jet Air Force Two was hurtling over the Pacific toward that beach. He squeezed her knee and poured a drop of milk into her tea, his eyes bright once again. "I'm going to have to spend a long session on deep background with the press contingent simply because they know all about this extended interview with you, even though they understand that it will not be published until at least April. But they claim that during the crisis the administration is using the London *Times* for leaks as a matter of policy. It doesn't matter how often I deny it."

"Is it true? Are you using me? I hope so."

"You are such a character. Come on, let's continue. Put on the tape (and move over there and keep the machine between us)," whispering and slipping his hand up underneath the loose-fitting dirndl to where her panties should have been. She cupped her hand over his and pressed. ("Quick, before it's too late," he mumbled in her ear, "we're only in—")

B.J-R.: —human . . . ah, Tape three, side one continued . . . Dr. Manheim, on Tuesday evening the President said that the present situation was *more* critical than the Cuban missile crisis. Do you agree with that?

WOLF MANHEIM: It depends on what your scale is. We could—

B.J-R.: Yes, quite, I know that you are fond of that analogy, and so I have a scale here for you to use. We must try in these matters, mustn't we? Very well. In 1947 the *Bulletin of the Atomic Scientists* first presented us with its famous "doomsday clock," and the hands read two minutes to midnight. Right. The hands were pictured at two minutes to midnight in the *Bulletin* in 1953 when it became known that both the U.S. and the USSR had developed the hydrogen bomb. In 1963 with the signing of the Partial Test Ban Treaty by President Kennedy, the scientists moved the clock hands back to twelve minutes to midnight—the record, by the way. By 1969 the hands were still back at ten minutes to midnight because of the ratification of the Nuclear Non-Proliferation Treaty. In 1974, we had slipped to nine minutes to midnight because India and Israel had the bomb. In 1980 the clock read seven minutes to midnight because of the Afghanistan scare, and that's where it has stayed for four years. Now if we argue that the Cuban missile crisis was a five- or four-minute-to-midnight situation, where would you as National Security Adviser put the hands of that clock today, January 19, 1984?

W.M.: . . . Eleven fifty-seven, P.M. . . .

B.J-R.: . . . That's extraordinary . . . You are saying for the record that according to your expert calculations that the world is within a diminished fraction of annihilation?

W.M.: I did not say "annihilation". We were talking about *tactical,* not strategic, nuclear weapons, I believe.

B.J-R.: Now look, the *Bulletin* clock that we're using for purposes of measurement is predicated on nuclear holocaust. The United States has secretly negotiated joint advisory control of all nuclear launching systems in China, according to Watson Colman's latest book, and he's an authority everybody over here seems to respect.

If that's true then why can't the U.S. guarantee to the Soviets that China would not be the first to fire such weapons?

W.M.: Accepting your premise and Mr. Colman's for argument's sake only, who is going to guarantee what the Soviet Union will or will not do? How could *we* "give away" China's option for survival in case of—

B.J-R.: Survival! You mean—

W.M.: I mean survival if the threat of a strike forces the Soviets to weigh the—

B.J-R.: Excuse me, Mr. Adviser, but at eleven fifty-seven P.M. there is precious little gap any more, barely a shadow between a threat and a reality.

W.M.: That is why the President has announced how seriously we view the situation and why I have been asked to privately brief both the PRC and the USSR.

B.J-R.: And what are you going to tell them?

W.M.: I am going to listen. And report back to the President and the NSC, and *then* the United States will make its position clear.

B.J-R.: And you do not rule out a U.S. position of alliance with China or of neutrality in the case of war—which might very easily trigger a Soviet preemptive strike or a Chinese provocation.

W.M.: To answer the first part of your question: the United States, at this point in time, rules out *no* position or option.

B.J-R.: How do you respond, then, to the charges leveled yesterday by Special Ambassador Georgi Arbatov, speaking for the Kremlin, that it is the U.S. that has destabilized the balance by—just a moment!—1) providing the PRC with heavy armament components, 2) covering up the South Africa-West German nuclear testing, 3) placing the most sophisticated nuclear warheads on West German soil, 4) sending covert CIA advisers to aid both the Afghan insurgents and the Pol Pot remnant in Cambodia, 5) threatening and blaming *both* Russia and Cuba over the chaos in Central America, despite U.N. findings to the contrary, 6) invoking laws to make mass arrests in California, Chicago and New York on Monday and Tuesday, and 7) the most important, the deployment

of an MX missile system in Japan—forcing the Japanese to rearm
—at the same time as both SALT II and III talks were scrapped?
W.M.: Yes, that is the Soviet line.
B.J-R.: Well, how do you answer it?
W.M.: At length.

Then began in earnest the debate—and it did not cease when the
Secret Service wheeled in pepper steaks for luncheon—that B. J-R
had been looking for from the start. In all of her major encounters
and interviews there seemed to come such a moment of passion, or
revelation, or both. Wick and the agents were irritated, then en-
raged that the one-hour interview went on long past the lunch
break, into the afternoon and over the Pacific to the approach to
the islands. Peter Wick—the brilliant best boy from Harvard, who
in turn ran a stable of eight in-house whiz kid gofers on the Manheim staff—was developing a full-fledged Iago complex, she decided. After all, she and Wolf *were* "making the beast with two
backs"; Wick had gathered that as soon as he heard about the
incident with the Chilean on Sunday. "That's right," she remembered, "Othello had the 'falling sickness,' too." She would, she
vowed, take care of the entire entourage in her essay if she could
ever get beyond this ever-deepening crisis.

But no interruption could stop them. Here were two strong
intellects and imaginations, matched in a kind of historic as well as
personal struggle. There was at once the quality of lovemaking and
combat about their argument—and some laughter—that Wick and
Jarrell and their boys could see in their flushed cheeks, bright eyes
and animated gestures. Pointing, standing; hunching shoulders.
Their voices sounded even in the forward cabins.

He began by lashing out at the revisionists of the years 1946–
1984. His version was Homeric—Stalinist Russia had stolen that
most seductive secret of nuclear power and thus had begun Amer-

ica's Iliad to recapture its leverage, its Helen, its geopolitical linkage. "Its luck," she chimed in.

Stalin had built on centuries of megalomaniacal czarist fantasies of expansion; the post-Brezhnev Kremlin was still acting out the same scenario. Wolf knew his Gogol and Dostoevski and brought up these pipeorgans of the Slavic soul into the attack against Betsy's revisionist apostasy. She, for her part, began to sound like Oscar Wilde reincarnate; so deadly was her aim and wicked her speech pattern that the recent *New Yorker* profile had likened her performances in words to "the young Noel Coward" (that was before anyone knew about her descent from Lord Russell).

"Dr. Manheim, you're being supercilious about the poor benighted Russians merely because they never quite had a *renaissance* —"

"Oh, stop playing devil's advocate. You know about how long you would last as an interviewer in the Soviet Union with your elegant hatchet jobs?"

"There is a tradition of reading there—"

"No, there is a 'tradition' of censorship and prison for writers there. Wasn't even Dostoevski hounded by the Czar's secret police until—"

"I can quote Dostoevski, too," she interrupted. " 'What if man is not altogether monstrous?' I mean, you know, the people you surround yourself with—young Dr. Wick and his molls may just be too clever by half, and let's face it, you depend on these droves of 'action intellectuals' for your data and your communication. And, besides, I'm not a real revisionist. I follow B.R.'s line, basically—you know, keep your eye on the bomb. Speaking of which, who guarantees against a *U.S.* first strike? You *are* the only ones to ever have dropped one, aren't you?"

"But what were the Russians ready to do in 1946? Do you know that their ambitions in Japan were such that today we would face a 'Tokyo Wall'? What would you think of an 'East Tokyo' in an 'East Japan'?"

"Not too pretty, but is it any worse than Japan as the stopper in the dirty bathtub of the Trilateral Commission? Has the U.S.-Western Europe-Japanese consortium done anything except make the world a giant Park Avenue and a giant Harlem?"

"Yes. It has avoided world war."

"What has?"

"U.S.-Trilateral-economic and military power has—"

"But not USSR power? Look, all these great men have managed, so far, not to blow up the world. Two cheers. My, haven't we progressed since the Pleistocene? Just don't try to sell me your party line, please, about Soviet devils—leave that to the royalists at Langley and MI-6."

At which the President's adviser lectured her sternly on "Finlandization" and "Czarist-Communist historico-political pan-Slavic crusades."

"Oh, balls," her voice was hoarse now, and Wick, who was peering around the corner from the stenography pool, winced and pulled back. "That's just a new version of the 'Missile Gap' and the 'Bomber Gap' and now, bless us, the 'Laser Gap'—I know that *you're* beyond that, but really, Wolf, I think you're just spouting holy writ."

He was being challenged as his eavesdropping aides had not heard him so before. She talked as the tape ran out and she changed it. Why, she demanded, had the USSR failed so miserably in Egypt, Afghanistan, Ethiopia, and, most of all, China.

The typing from the pool stopped as if this time there might actually be an answer forthcoming. She quoted B.R., and George Orwell—"Oh, what a place, what a people, what a civilization!"

Wolf felt himself driven on. He was still most at home in the German pantheon and his version of the Cold War was studded with echoes from Freud and Marx and Nietzsche. He stood up again. ". . . You're dealing with mass phenomena. The 'age of atoms' is still the age of the Nation-State, *that* is the reality beyond ideologies. . . . Listen, in the fifties we feared the Soviet-Chinese combined forces, in the sixties we tilted toward the Russians against the Chinese, and since the seventies it's the other way. President Kennedy actually called for a study on the feasibility of a strike against Chinese nuclear installations before they had developed SAM capacity—(that has to come out of the printed version of this) —the point being, in the end, that we couldn't do that because of the uncertainty of what the Soviet reaction would be. Well now *they,* the Soviets, are going much further than a feasibility study and we have to make use of the fact *that they don't know what our response would be.* And that goes for the PRC as well. That was Zbig's fatal weakness, his hatred for the Russians was obsessive."

"Whereas yours is rational?"

"Remember, I was liberated at Buchenwald by Russians, my father's mother was a Russian Jew who migrated to Germany—"

"Tell me something about your family?" she asked abruptly.

"Later (tonight)."

"All right, then, you have to let me finish this cassette—we're days behind in the taping and we're stuck in this crisis . . . There. Right. Now—

BETSY JONES-RUSSELL: —now . . . can we talk about your concentration camp experience?

WOLFGANG MANHEIM: I prefer not.

B.J-R.: . . . very well. In that case, Dr. Manheim, isn't it time to state honestly what the United States considers to be her policy—not her rhetoric but her actual *policy,* warts and all—vis-à-vis world war. For instance, much as you dislike answering this, was the use of atomic weapons in Japan justified?

W.M.: The dropping of the bombs on Hiroshima and Nagasaki was a success. It ended the war. It also became the first major operation of the diplomatic cold war with Russia still in progress today. We are paying a price, of course, for changing our position on the use of nuclear weapons. That is why I have been asked to talk to the PRC and the Soviets in order that there be no dangerous ambiguity.

B.J-R.: But Dr. Manheim, America is a democracy and as we talk there are reports that campuses and inner cities are erupting. In short, will you tell the American *people* what you intend to do, as well as your opposite numbers in Beijing and Moscow?

W.M.: That is surely part of the purpose of these interviews. (I see you are smiling.)

B.J-R.: (Yes, with irony and a bit of pleasure . . .) Then I must put to you a problematic question. Is it not a fact that United States policy, since Hiroshima, *was and is and has always been to threaten use of nuclear weapons?* In short, the "Madman Theory"—despite public protestations to the contrary.

W.M.: Where shall I start?

B.J-R: Hiroshima.

W.M.: We've already talked about Hiroshima, haven't we?

B.J-R.: Not really. What Hiroshima suggests is not that a liberal humane society can make a *mistake* and commit mass murder but that it is *characteristic* for modern societies to do so . . . Dr. Manheim, you are being extremely frank and so I want to ask you in all seriousness whether you think this policy, and the men that have spawned and practiced it, are quite *sane?*

W.M.: That is the wrong question. What you should ask is—"is this *survival,* as we know it, at this stage of human development?" And the answer to that is yes.

B.J-R.: Is this "the unfolding of historical necessity in China," as you wrote in 1982?

W.M.: I wrote that an intensified conflict with Moscow was liable to shift China toward the side of the American effort, since it would present them with the only way to undercut Soviet influence in Asia. And that, again, concert between the United States and China over Southeast Asia could be expected to encourage the

Soviet Union to move closer to the United States on the Middle East. And that the United States as the leader of the free world—"

B.J-R.: Step back into the ranks of ordinary people and you can see all too clearly what all heads of state and their intellectual hired guns are.

Well, haven't we arrived at Orwell's *1984?* "WAR IS PEACE." Superpower vs. superpower. The planet divided into three zones— Oceania, Eurasia and Eastasia—in a state of permanent conflict designed to divert attention from domestic matters. Today, NATO, the Warsaw Pact and the Third World, including China, offer a parallel. Much of Orwell's predicted weaponry is now plausible. He talked about lenses in space, for instance. Room 101, where 1984's behavior-modification horrors took place, was in the "Ministry of Love." Which brings us to "terrorist chic," and the current fascination with sadomasochistic fashion displays and the more bizarre spectacles of punk and pornography.

W.M.: Have you ever considered interviewing yourself?

The end-of-tape warning buzzed. Peter Wick and James Jarrell were white-faced with disapproval. As Wolf left the cabin, she began to think about the path across the beach and the bright moon over Waikiki.

Andrew Kott stood in the dim, short corridor leading to the lavatory. As Wolf turned into the area, talking over his shoulder, he almost stepped on the much shorter man. "Andy," Wolf smiled. The young aide stared at him with wide eyes. He had been listening. Worldlessly he flattened himself against the plastic wall and inched away past the National Security Adviser, all the while staring up at him. Wolf watched him go, heard him say something to Betsy in the cabin.

Wolf's smile faded. The strain was starting to break Andy Kott. During the war games in Room 11, the cherubic face had, for the first time he could remember, stayed stiff and silent. Kott had a raw-boned young wife from Texas and a retarded child, and that was constant pressure. Let him talk to Betsy, he thought angrily without knowing why, let him show her his pathetic snapshots of the wife and the little girl posed in front of the Supreme Court. And the photo of the three of them taken by "Uncle Wolf."

Wolf locked the toilet door; the pale illumination cast a bluish tinge over his skin. He avoided his reflection in the mirror. The washroom was four times the size of an ordinary airliner's. Compulsively, his eyes picked at the trade name on the toilet bowl— Crown. He was smiling again as he let his trousers slip down. Then the smile seemed to freeze on his face.

Sitting on the commode, the chemical odor made Wolf remember the smell of carbolic acid in the hospital at Buchenwald. Gooseflesh rose in a band across his forehead, inside he went numb. The exhilaration of the contest with B.J-R. was driven out of him and his forehead tightened.

"To each his own," he breathed, remembering . . .

9

BUCHENWALD—EARLY SPRING, 1944

"TO EACH HIS OWN." The sign posted over the gate to the Buchenwald complex meant nothing to the boy. It was not like the legend of Auschwitz—"WORK MAKES YOU FREE" according to Dr. Manheim—it simply meant nothing, yet Wolfgang could not help staring at it and saying the words over to himself under his breath. He was repeating this nonsense silently as he hurried out of his warm, clean cubicle at the hospital to follow the medical chief to the truck.

The train bearing new prisoners would have stopped in Weimar to let out a few civilians, and the prisoners would have heard the church bells. When he, the boy, had come from Berlin, he had heard the church bells ring out and seen the slow, sly faces peeking from their windows at the new inmates of the camp. He had traveled through dense forests, dark green and sooty-white along the tracks, until the shouts and clanging brought the new ones to the camp station and the first thing they saw as they scrambled out of the cars was "TO EACH HIS OWN." What did it mean?

101

Today the boy stamped his feet and hugged his new coat close. Before Father Thyle, the little monk, had gone "to give Jesus Christ a tour of the Bunker and got himself strangled," according to the doctor, he had left his coat and a message for Wolfie. The coat fit snugly but the message was a paradox and it worried him, the same way as the sign did. What the monk had told Dr. Manheim to tell, or rather ask, the boy was, "Does God need man?" The cold air carried the strains of the camp orchestra—Mozart—to the boy's ears.

Some SS genius, also according to the doctor, had posted a fresh travesty for the new arrivals to see, a brutal caricature of a Catholic priest, a Communist, and a Jew dancing. The priest looked a bit like the little monk to the boy, and the Jew—not the Communist, but the *Jew*—clearly resembled his father—big and shaggy. Wolfgang thought, "I look like my mother though I am tall for my age." Then, as always lately, he put his mother and the old apartment on the Kaiserdamm out of his consciousness by repeating the slogan "TO EACH HIS OWN," over and over.

The arrivals walked slowly through the ranks of machine guns toward the looming stone buildings fifty meters ahead. The boy carried the doctor's big orderly book. The ground was frozen and occasionally he slid, but the new ones walked so slowly and with such cautious childlike steps that no one fell. In the silence, the panting, sweating engine was like a huge beast on the tundra. Dr. Manheim moved through the thin, frozen crowd, ostensibly marking out the sick and half-dead or more—they all looked to be at least half-dead. Actually he was attempting to identify Communists while there was still time to warn them what to do and say until the camp "underground" could get in touch with them.

Wolfgang had been under the charge of the little monk, and then in the doctor's office at the hospital, so he was very hazy in his mind about what the Communists or the "underground" really did in the camp, and saw only what the doctor permitted him to see.

The arrivals shuffled to a halt at the gate to the quarantine. Some would have collapsed if not for red-starred men who braced those who could go on no longer. The few SS stayed close to the stove in the guardhouse. They knew the drill by heart. Then, as he did almost every day, Dr. Manheim addressed the strangers, the breath streaming out of his mouth like smoke.

"You have arrived at Buchenwald. Soon enough you'll learn the difference between Auschwitz and Buchenwald. Comradeship is law number one here. Most of us are political prisoners; on the whole, you are not. But you, too, were compelled to leave your country by the same force which drove us here. All of us are *victims.* That is why we must be united . . . The SS command did not provide any rations for you tonight. But the Norwegian students,
when they heard of your arrival this afternoon, offered to give up their bread rations to you. Our French comrades have offered their portion of margarine for today. The Yugoslav group will be fetching some hot soup before long. Everybody will get his provisions in exactly equal measure; nobody gets less, and no one may get more. It is forbidden to swap about with your food rations; what they give us is little enough in any case, and every bit is needed to survive at all. . . . Probably you'll only stay in Buchenwald for a short while, after which you'll be sent out to work at one of the outer camps. But while you are here, and let us hope afterwards, too, you will live according to the laws of Buchenwald."

The boy followed the doctor, jotting down what he was told; such information as "M. Lazolav—Printer" and then other words that the boy knew were some sort of codified description of the man's political history. Today's arriving group had been less than a hundred, all men, and now they fell on their food with sobs of hunger. The food disappeared. The boy and the doctor left them to the charge of the camp kapos and the SS death gangs for processing, except for three who the doctor demanded be removed at once to the hospital, though they appeared to the boy rather more alive than the others.

As he hurried out after the doctor, the boy could hear the arguments beginning:

"The Reds run the show—"

"They feed you and now it's 'the Reds'—"

"Yes. At Auschwitz you former capitalist managers and informers had your chance and—"

"The Nazis are anticapitalist too, why not—"

"*Ha!* Moron, idiot—"

The doctor chuckled, but the boy knew that there was truth in it. The Communists held sway in the offices, kitchens, barracks and officers' quarters, besides their nest of power in the hospital. There were cells and meetings, only semisecret; the SS could never run the major industry that was Buchenwald without the Communists. *L'univers concentrationnaire*—to quote a French comrade who served as Dr. Manheim's agent in the Commandant's office—this Buchenwald was a self-contained world. Over against his previous life, this other world was drawing the boy irreversibly toward its center. Though he was, as yet, sleepwalking in the broad-backed shadow of his guide, the doctor-father, and the memory of the little monk, his holy ghost. The French comrade, Lucien Hellman, would corner him to give catechism, while in his mind the boy whispered, "To each his own."

First, then, came the Communists. Under them, the Social Democrats. Then the capitalists and the clergy, always excepting, of course, "saints like Father Thyle." Then there were the homosexuals, who were all killed, and the thieves, jailbirds, Jehovah's Witnesses . . . and apart from all, the Jews. The struggle for control of the camp had been between criminals and Communists and it had been savage. The Communists, under Dr. Manheim's leadership, had held a tenuous control since early 1942 and, whispered the

Frenchman, "as the Russians get closer there will be another shift in the basic relationship of forces . . ." but the boy could not guess what *that* would be—to each his own?

Things ran smoothly now (the SS came into the camp in force only for the *appell,* the daily headcounts), but before it had been very different. Buchenwald and its satellite base camps had been built by the slave labor of thousands—long since incinerated and gone up the chimneys of the camp crematorium after having been worked or tortured to madness and death. The years had taken their toll on the SS as well: they stole and drank and fornicated themselves into a kind of stupor, leaving to the political prisoners the mundane workings of the death camp. Communist clerks of German origin were "selected for," Comrade Hellman murmured.

"I know what that means," the boy said, "my mother was an anthropologist."

The *L'univers concentrationnaire,* the main Economic and Administrative Office, Department D, carefully classified all camps as Class I, II, or III. Class III, of course, represented the "mills of death" like Auschwitz, while Buchenwald had been a II but was changed to a I, three months after the boy's arrival, to a mere forced labor camp. All the boy knew was that the place was still so dangerous that his father warned him against even leaving the hospital without him to talk to any of the other children.

Hundreds of thousands of children lived and died in the world of the camps. During Wolfgang's time there were less than nine hundred minors left at Buchenwald, the youngest a three-and-a-half-year-old Polish boy whose file card listed him as a "partisan." Before the little monk had disappeared, he and Wolfgang had used to make up a bed behind the stove for the "partisan" and give him scraps of food. Now Dr. Manheim told Wolfgang to forget about little Androszha, as the monk had called him—kissing the pale cheek and making the sign of the cross, unseen, over the child's white-haired head.

Wolfgang did not learn from his mentors that the sexual abuse of children by SS and criminals had reached such a depth of degradation by 1943. Little by little the boy began to pick up the cues and signals of how to behave as a "political animal." From veterans in the hospital the boy came to know at least the outline of the saga of the death camps. He learned that Buchenwald was almost a paradise compared to the camp IIIs in the East. Here, at least, if you could survive the labor gangs and were not a homosexual or a non-Communist Jew, there was work and shelter in the laundry or tailor shop or carpenter shop or orderly rooms. Most of the work consisted of making luxury goods for the SS. "Corruption is our salvation," repeated the Frenchman. The party line of the Communist camp managers was to promote graft always and everywhere —not only to make the SS increasingly dependent on inmate services and luxuries, but in order to actively subvert and blackmail senior officers. This had long since been accomplished, through morphine and sex, with the SS medical staff at the hospital.

To this end also in the "geneology details," scores of prisoners were kept occupied manufacturing tables of ancestors and family chronicles for the new lords of the SS. Beautifully tailored civilian suits and nonregulation uniforms were in constant demand by the dandies of the death-head elite. Whole suites of expensive furniture were crafted in order to outfit SS living quarters. Later, the boy would discover the uses of the brothel in the economy of corruption on which the lives of the survivors depended.

Those like the gypsies or the Jews, excluded from the riches of corruption, led an altogether different life. They were whipped like animals as they tore themselves apart hauling back-breaking rocks to make a wall and then break it down again under the SS truncheons, only to be driven to drag the rocks back to their original location. They were harnessed like horses to heavily laden wagons and lashed on at double time. They were drowned in pits of excrement, set on fire to run as human torches into the barbed wire, pushed into rock quarries, torn apart and eaten by SS killer dogs —all listed as "shot while trying to escape." And all the while the inmate orchestra played its daily medley, from music hall to Mozart.

The political prisoners in the corrupt headquarter brigades often worked only yards away from hideous scenes of sadism and murder. And every day ranks of inmates from the East marched past on their way to work as slaves for German war industries. Buchenwald brigades slaved as far away as the Channel Islands; other thousands were worked to death on the Rhine. The boy watched them march by each day like the walking dead, the *musselmen*. The headquarters kapos measured the labor brigades differently than the boy—every man was credited for every hour of work, with the money going directly to the SS, a million and a half marks a month to Buchenwald alone. Again, they could be counted up as, every day, hundreds of skeletons were trucked back to camp for cremation.

The boy told himself that he was safe, along with his father, at the very center of the camp Hospital and Sanitation Service. The boy's chief responsibility was to help one of the medical orderlies innoculate incoming prisoners against typhoid fever and dysentery. Commandant Koch was fond of proclaiming in his hoarse shout, "There are no sick men in my camp. They are either well or dead!"

So fearful were the SS of the raging epidemics that swept the camps that Dr. Manheim needed only to mark an inmate down as infected and no guard would come near him as long as he lived in one of the quarantined hospital wards. In this way the political prisoners were taken under the wing of the "Manheim Operation." These men, many of them notables who had been in their countries' diplomatic service, carried on marathon talkfests in the wards, and Dr. Manheim often sent the boy in to listen and "absorb some realpolitik." Such was the boy's unique *Gymnasium*.

Each morning sick prisoners trudged to the center of the grove where the hospital stood, often snowed in or awash in a mud slide. Nevertheless, the inmates, who were never to use the gravel path, stood in silent lines in the open, waiting for an orderly.

First an SS guard kicked out of line those who looked to him to be malingering. Hours later the SS medical officer would arrive, drunk, to curse, slap and kick the remnant. Then he would stagger off and the inmate orderlies would do what they could: "Above the waist—aspirin; below—castor oil." Only political prisoners had been privately admitted into the hospital by the underground, and these lucky ones might remain hidden in the contagious wards for three or four years, their identity papers long since "fixed" by comrades in the offices of the Headquarters Company.

The facilities were clean, carbolic and rudimentary. All the dentists were fully occupied pulling gold teeth out of the mouths of dead prisoners, so there was no time for those whose teeth were infected. "But it is much worse at Auschwitz," the boy was assured by the Frenchman. "There, they await the doctor, lying naked on a concrete floor—arranged by nationality rather than symptoms. I swear it! When his honor the Camp Medical Officer deigns to put in an appearance, he reviews the poor bastards, calling to an aide, 'Right-Left-Right-Left.' Those on the left are given fatal injections out of hand." The boy liked the Frenchman chiefly because he was teaching him to speak French by songs and verses:

> *Un—deux—trois, nous irons au bois*
> *quatre—cinq—six, cueillir des cerises*
> *sept—huit—neuf, dans un panier neuf*
> *dix—onze—douze, elles seront toutes rouges*

Even such simple learning rhymes could help drown out that infernal ditty going round and round in his head—"to each his own."

All the while Dr. Manheim ran the far-flung camp underground from his crowded carbolic-smelling office, and not even the *Waffen-*

SS doctors and medical officers dared to go too far against Manheim's always politely phrased wishes. And his written records were law.

No one felt compelled to mention to the boy that Special Infirmary 49 was given over to human vivisection. Here the truly mad doctors Neumann and Eysele brought inmates that they had abducted at will. Then followed amputations, resections, exploratory operations, all without anesthetic. Even German band music could not drown out the shrieks, so that all the boy could do was to sing in his mind's ear, *"To each his own, to each his own . . ."*

Of course, the boy had no idea of what was being done in the name of medical science at Auschwitz, Dachau, Sachsenhausen, Natzweiler; or at Ravensbrück to the girls and women; or that the ghastly tortures took place under the aegis of such well-known corporations as I.G. Farben and Behrung Works, as well as the most famous scientific and university institutes in Germany, which was to say in all of Europe. Sometimes the atrocities were discussed in Ward 50, but when the boy entered, the subject was immediately changed even though the Ward was virtually secure. Still, he came inevitably to know it all, in his *Gymnasium* of death. Especially he knew how necessary it was to be a Communist and not a Jew or a half Jew, and why Father Thyle had said that "Man is the Jew." . . . "Jews believe in God," whispered comrade Hellman, "but God is dead. The devil is still alive, though, in Ward 50."

Ward 50 was widely advertised as the terminal TB ward, and as such no SS in his right mind, or prison informer either, would go anywhere near it. Actually, Ward 50 was the nerve center of the camp underground. In the regular course of routine, corpses from the Special Autopsy Section were rerouted through Ward 50 with false identities so that the appearance of virtual plague could be maintained. The small ward housed men marked for death by the SS at any given time, as well as coded files in a locked alcove that served as a secret office for Dr. Manheim. Wolfgang had been told never to enter Ward 50 without knocking first. On the day that he overheard the conversation, he had already lifted his hand to knock and call out his own name when he recognized the two voices.

He froze when he caught the rasping tone and penetrating diction of the man who had raised him, Luftwaffe Colonel Ernst Hoder, the man he had now been told was his stepfather. When at length the sharp staccato stopped, the answering voice was that of his new father, his real father, Dr. Manheim. Despite his strained attention the boy could make out only snatches of dialogue through the heavy double doors. At the same time he had to be on the lookout; a passing officer would be instantly suspicious of anyone found loitering at the door of the dreaded Ward 50. The hearing problem was further complicated by the omnipresent phonograph recordings—today it was Wagner's *Tristan and Isolde in Nurenburg*—played over the corridor speakers for reasons of security.

". . . Treblinka . . . hand grenades and . . . machine pistols with money from camp sources . . . justify more than one or two visits to the boy without bringing suspicion on . . ."

Suddenly, the doctor's deep voice grew low and intense so that the boy could gather even less. Something about "debts and arrangements made years ago." Then again the blurred burst from the colonel.

"I owe you *nothing!* I have more than . . . How do you think I feel . . . An Air Force officer, not some beer-hall . . . his own flesh and blood . . . After all, it was I who . . . Hilda in the last years . . ."

Hilda! The boy's dead mummy's name. Wolfgang stumbled away from the door. "I have a toothache of the soul"—he remembered the little monk's diagnosis as he was sick in the carbolic-acid-smelling utility closet across from Ward 50.

10

KAHALA, HAWAII—JANUARY 19, 1984
(THURSDAY NIGHT)

"If you say the stars are like diamonds over Diamond Head or that the warm air is positively sensual and caresses the skin, I'll scream. Give me your arm, I want to take my shoes off. Can the Secret Service boys see us from there? Thank God it's dark and we don't have to dodge the cops, and the demonstrators chanting '*Haole* go home!' "

They both took off their shoes and continued on across the white sand toward the water. "I have to believe," she looked up at him, "that a night of bougainvillea, bright yellow and peach colored, and a rain forest of greens and ferns around the B.O.Q., to say nothing of the wild orchids, and the mountains, and the mountains of clouds and that pregnant moon, the trade winds and the fish-filled sea, etc., etc., that all this is in the service of making love and not war. That is why my plan is to bind you in the carnal chains of nature, of my body, thereby striking at least a glancing blow for survival." She

111

ruffled his fine hair with her free hand. The warm wind played with their clothes and hair as they paused to look at each other. The cool jazz sounds of a Teddy Nash bossa nova from the hotel just reached them.

"Part Pulitzer prize, part purple prose, part poetry. B.J., you are unlike any woman I have ever known. I would almost rather hear you talk than anything else."

"Almost?"

"Almost." He wrapped his arm around her. Her hips seemed to rise to meet his hands as she leaned into him with her breasts and the mound of her sex. Her tongue traced at the corner of his wide mouth until he pushed past her lips to explore her. She could feel his breath in warm jets on her cheek as they kissed, and his sex bulging against her belly. She stayed close to him, then reached up to touch his brow and to say carefully, "On Sunday, Wolf . . . when that terrible thing happened, at first I thought that you had knocked yourself out in falling. But it was *petit mal,* whatever that catchall means, wasn't it? I only bring it up because I care for you and I'm concerned about what this crisis is doing to you, and because I see how you're driving yourself night and day, and I don't want to add to your burden with my bloody interview and—"

He kissed her raised hand and arm, then again his lips and tongue merged with her mouth, more gently this time. Then he said, "You're helping me, B.J." His eyes in the full moonlight looked more sad, vulnerable, than she had yet seen. "I don't mean in the sense of using you to leak official positions—but I *am* 'using' you in another way, a, ah, human way, in the way of—"

"In the way of love?"

"Yes. I guess so. If I can love . . ."

Her silence was a question as they started to walk again. The sound of the waves echoed in the cove. The security men were out of sight now, somewhere on the stone walkways, pretending to lean against the palm trees, sipping mai tais or banana daiquiris. "Maybe a coconut will fall on Jarrell's head," she almost said as the silence dragged on, but she sensed that he was working up to something.

At the ocean's edge they let the water lap at their feet. He looked out to sea as he spoke. "That blackout on Sunday was one of the worst. I didn't remember a thing until you went over it all. You didn't know that, did you? These migraines or whatever the hell it is—the doctors don't know—started after I was liberated from Buchenwald. You see, my father was a Jew but he was also the camp doctor so we were together in the camp hospital and we were safe there until the summer of '44, then they . . . took him away and I was sent back to Berlin to relatives, and, ah . . ."

"In '44!?"

The words had tumbled out just above the splashing of the water. The jazz band from the hotel could not reach them here. In the silence he stared out over the dark moon-streaked sea.

"Yes. It's amazing, isn't it? My mother was already dead."

"In the camp?"

"No, no, she wasn't Jewish. Before I went to the camp. But, afterwards, that's when the headaches began. And then later in Chicago. After the war . . ."

"Headaches," she thought, the doctor on the telephone from London had spoken to her of the ancient and still mysterious affliction: of trances, fugues and psychic blackouts, of *petit* and *grand mal,* of comas and falling sickness and of how the blood fled from the brain in order to spare that delicate organ from thoughts that were too painful to bear. "It allows the body to play dead, if you take my meaning," the doctor had concluded. She took the meaning, a camouflage of the nervous system, perhaps . . .

A sawing breath escaped him and she knew that he wasn't going to say anymore about the past that night. "And love?" she asked, taking his hand.

"You think love would cure me?"

"Love could probably cure us all," she said.

He gripped her hand. "I'm beginning to feel something very unusual, for me, for *you,*" he said.

Her intuition told her to let him off the hook of his past for a moment. "So," she smiled, "you and my mother both grew up in Chicago?"

"That's right . . . And you owe me my bedtime story. Back to B.R."

"Right. Back to B.R." They began to walk around the curve of the shore, further from the hotel. It can't be so bad, she thought, or he'd be in the Pearl Harbor Naval Station code room now, talking to the White House or the Pentagon. She lifted her arms wide to let the sweet air bathe her.

"Let's see, I told you that my mother ran away to Spain to join the Abraham Lincoln Brigade. By all accounts she was a remarkable woman and an immediate favorite of the big guns there, like Hemingway and, of course, George Orwell. She certainly had an affair with Orwell. As I understand it, he and Hemingway and that lot took a different position than Lillian Hellman and the Communists, and they all hated each other only slightly less than they all hated the Fascists. (I used to fancy that Orwell was my father. I still wonder . . .) And ma saw it all at Brunete and Aragon.

"She used to say that the Fascist bombardment of Barcelona broke their hearts, and, of course, the bloody English wouldn't let Leon Blum declare war against Italy. You know, they machine-gunned the civilian population from the air. Churchill was horrified, but, of course, Chamberlain had sold out and the U.S. was, at that stage, of no use. Those were *my* bedtime stories: hand-to-hand at Granada, and the International Brigade officers who ordered retreat and were shot by their own men—and women. Then, November and farewell to the International Brigade. Marching down Ramblas while the people of Barcelona wept and cheered and threw flowers . . . *La Pasionaria's* final oration to the veterans and the throng. I know every word of the close. She, my mother, used to stand up and sing it in Spanish and English. It was, without question, the climax of her life; everything after Spain was only memory for her. While other children were learning about the Cold War, I was being taught rhetoric and history and politics from the speeches of *La Pasionaria.*"

He stopped a few yards away from her to take in the presence of this astonishing woman who, in remembering her mother remembering the great Spanish woman, the "Passionate One," seemed transfigured where she stood on the wet sand. Her hair shone in the moonlight as thunder clouds gathered over her head. Her voice was vibrant, penetrating him.

"*Mujeres! Madres!* Women! Mothers! When the years pass and the wounds of the war are staunched . . . then speak to your children. Tell them of the International Brigade. Tell them how, coming over seas and mountains, crossing frontiers, bristling with bayonets, they reached our country as crusaders of freedom. They gave up everything, their homes, their country . . . and they came and told us: 'We are here; your cause, Spain's cause, is ours. It is the cause of all advanced and progressive mankind.' Today they are going away. Many of them, thousands of them, are staying here with the Spanish earth for their shroud . . . You can go proudly. *You are history. You are legend! . . .*"

She could not finish and buried herself in his arms. His legs braced as he caught and held her. "At least she lived to tell—" he tried to comfort her.

"No, she died there. She took sleeping pills in 1955 but she died *there.*" Slowly, she became aware that he was moved too. "God," she sighed, "it's been years since I let go like that. Not since B.R. died . . ."

"Or me," he said and kissed her. "I'm remembering Barcelona," he said, his mouth moving in her hair, "and Munich and Chamberlain and I'm trying to hold the line before it's too late."

She let that pass. She was spent. "Take me back to my hotel, Wolf, and shake the SS, and hold me and make love to me very gently, and then sneak back to the embassy and sleep on the plane tomorrow. Will you do that for me, my love?"

11

BEIJING—JANUARY 22, 1984
(SUNDAY)

James Jarrell was the executive officer of the United States Secret Service Protective Reaction Group (PRG) charged with the security of Wolfgang Manheim, code name "Tower." Jarrell was, however, in fact primarily responsible to A. D. Winston, the Deputy Director of Operations—the clandestine section—of the Central Intelligence Agency. In addition to his routine security coordination of the "Tower" PRG team of nine agents, it was Jarrell's assignment to filter information to the Agency at Langley regarding Manheim and all his private and political activities. This he did, unknown to the President or to his National Security Adviser.

Wolf Manehim knew, of course, in a general way, that he was not only the brain of the National Security Agency, but its creature as well. Competing agencies had been spying on each other in the United States since World War II; that was understood. When Presidents and their senior advisers wished to speak to each other confidentially, they stepped out into the Rose Garden—and kept walking. Wolf had stood in that garden and at Camp David whispering—about the PRC and the USSR, and war and peace—in rain and sleet and snow since late November.

The President was convinced that the Defense Intelligence Agency as well as Central Intelligence were spying on the executive branch, sabotaging it, setting it up. So, for what it was worth, Wolf watched his back. Yet in the Washington game of taps and leaks he understood the rules even better than most of his rivals. He understood that the "leaks" were merely a variation on the theme of information and communications theory. Information could be more powerful than secrecy, he believed, when it flowed out in a controlled and coherent way. His adversaries could count their electronically purloined secrets like so many misers fingering smooth gold coins; he, Wolf Manheim, would use a Betsy Jones-Russell to finesse them, to flush out the secrecy mongers with information . . . with the truth—as he saw it. As far as he was concerned, Jarrell could be working for the KGB—it would still work.

In the service of this double role as CIA penetration agent within the Secret Service, Jarrell, under the guise of "Advance Security," caused miniature listening devices to be installed in the mansion of the Chinese millionaire, Sang Hobang. He caused this to be done in advance of the first private meeting between Wolfgang Manheim and Vice-Chairman Hu Ziping, the chief strategist for the People's Republic of China. This covert task was quickly accomplished by Jarrell, since it was executed with the connivance of Mr. Sang.

Sang was a suave and sophisticated magnate who wore expensively tailored Mao suits in the most subtle of eggshell colors. Before the revolution, Sang, the last of his line, had inherited a linen producing empire from his aristocratic family. In the 1960s, during the rampages of the Cultural Revolution, Red Guards attacked and humiliated Sang's father and forced him to sweep public streets with a horsehair broom. By the time of Richard Nixon's first election in 1968, Mr. Sang had been not only restored to his financial eminence but promoted to the level of powerful liaison to Western, and especially American, leaders of industry.

It was this elegant ambassador's role to entertain and negotiate with his opposite numbers from New York, Berlin, Paris, London, and Rome. Of the more than one hundred fifty millionaires in the PRC, Sang was considered by all to be the first among unequals and the man to see in most matters of any delicacy that involved trade or money. As many as one hundred thousand middle-line capitalists, or "national bourgeoisie," had been rehabilitated after the deaths of Mao and Chou. These former "black class," along with such "nonpersons" as landlords, rich peasants, rightists, and "bad elements," were all hard at work by the 1980s generating capital, much of it foreign, for the PRC's great "Modernization for Security" plan or, precisely, "Second Leap Forward."

Sang's family estate, on the outskirts of Beijing, rose around spacious courtyards and ranks of formal gardens, famous for their experimental yellow and blue roses. Beyond the gardens, there were stables full of thoroughbred riding horses. In the mansion, servants and craftsmen maintained a permanent display of priceless antiques and dynastic artifacts, and prepared a table famous for its native dishes and Western wines.

The private meetings between Wolfgang Manheim and Hu Ziping were scheduled to begin after breakfast on the day following the arrival at the new Red Star Airport of the American delegation— plenty of time for James Jarrell and Chinese experts to activate the latent listening devices invisibly studded in the antique furniture of the second floor den, where the talks were scheduled to commence on Monday morning.

The world press was forced to station itself at the gates of the mansion at the bottom of a long and curving drive, landscaped by the Japanese genius Kurwikaya. Only B.J. Russell's considerable personal popularity in the ranks of the Fourth Estate had prevented an open rebellion over the week-long news blackout by the entire executive level of the government of the United States. Thanks to Russell, they knew all too well, the London *Times* had been able to front page leaks, on "deep background," about the continuing crisis under their star's photo-byline. Two banner headlines, in particular, had probably already assured Russell of still another Pulitzer prize. Reporters and commentators were filled with both professional awe and personal envy to read in the *Times* that "U.S. MAY TELL PRC TO RELY ON U.N.," and the following day— the day of the actual arrival of the American delegation in China —"NATO FORCES ON SECRET ALERT."

Thus a crowd of electronic and print media correspondents and technicians from around the world stamped about in near-freezing dudgeon at the gates of Sang's manor house by 9 A.M. on the morning of the first meeting. As always, the wind was out of the north. The throng included the anchormen of all three major American networks. At 9:15 A.M. the voice of CBS, Dan Rather, arrived with B. J. Russell by chauffeur-driven limousine. All eyes were on these two media luminaries, each bareheaded in thick fur coats—hers simple, emphasizing the A-line—as they alighted and quickly began to mingle and greet old friends. The evening before, in the Beijing Hotel, Rather had shyly modeled his mink-collared and cuffed winter Mao suit.

Later that night she dictated a background story to London that commanded front pages again the next day while the world waited for the talks to begin. She used a "safe telephone," courtesy of the National Security Adviser, at the executive office of Ford Motor Company.

"Hello, Richard—put Pamela on too, please. Give this to rewrite and insert it into the long piece on the genesis of the crisis between the U.S., China and the Soviets. Caps: WORLD WAR III INEVI-TABLE, CHINESE LEADER SAYS—WASHINGTON (DASH) CHINESE VICE CHAIRMAN HU WARNED IN AN EXCLUSIVE INTERVIEW WITH THE LONDON TIMES

THAT A THIRD WORLD WAR COULD START (QUOTE) ALMOST ANYWHERE (CLOSE QUOTE) BUT THAT THE MIDDLE EAST AND INDOCHINA ARE THE MOST LIKELY TROUBLE SPOTS (PERIOD) (SUBHEAD) WAR IN 1984 (PARA) LATER (COMMA) HE SAID (COMMA) (QUOTE) PRECISELY BECAUSE BOTH SIDES HAVE SO MANY NUCLEAR WEAPONS (COMMA) THE POSSIBILITY EXISTS THAT THE THIRD WORLD WAR WILL BE A CONVENTIONAL WAR (COMMA) NOT A NUCLEAR WAR (PERIOD CLOSE QUOTE) (PARA) MR. HU MADE IT CLEAR HE BELIEVES THE SOVIET UNION WILL BE RESPONSIBLE FOR THE NEXT GLOBAL CONFLICT (PERIOD PARA) (QUOTE) ONLY TWO COUNTRIES IN THE WORLD ARE CAPABLE OF LAUNCHING A WAR (COMMA) THE UNITED STATES AND THE SOVIET UNION (PERIOD CLOSE QUOTE). . . ."

In Sang Hobang's mansion, in a locked and guarded room one level beneath the one in which Wolf Manheim and Hu Zuping would meet in the morning, James Jarrell adjusted a meter that read TAPE SPEED . . . .

At 9:30 servants wheeled out portable coffee containers and plastic cups, and old China hands shook their heads sadly. At 9:47 the American Secret Service caravan honked its way through the reporters and cameramen, followed by an oversized official black Cadillac with four small American flags flapping in the freezing wind. Inside the limousine, National Security Adviser Wolfgang Manheim, in a gray fur greatcoat, stared straight ahead, looking bone grim to the suddenly silent men and women of the press. Next came smaller limousines carrying Peter Wick, Andrew Kott, and the rest of the Manheim brain trust (only the Anglo-American press could identify them and spell their names for their foreign colleagues). At 9:52 Vice-Chairman Hu's delegation arrived in a cavalcade of four deluxe Citroens. Now it was the Asian correspondents' turn to spell out names for the Western and Third World press. The tiny man in the blue cap, they said, was Hu Ziping.

Inside the meeting room where the two delegations crowded uncertainly, the American leader, Wolf Manheim, towered above all the others. Official photographers circled the perimeter, snapping as Mr. Hu and Dr. Manheim, posed in an awkward handshake, stared grimly into the lenses. Mr. Sang ushered off the small crowd of senior aides down the corridor and toward a buffet where Western dishes, exquisitely prepared, were spread out in a drawing room of imposing proportions.

The President's adviser found himself alone with Mr. Hu and realized with a start that the translators too had been steered out and down the corridor, and that Mr. Hu was going to speak in English and *alone* to the United States. Wolf smiled, sat and sampled the warm tea. At least, he reflected, the American translator, who was more often than not the CIA's creature, had been excluded.

The American smiled grimly and down at Mr. Hu's dull polished shoes, the size of a twelve-year-old's in the States. By this time Wolf had expected the little giant to have disappeared into Quin Chenge No. 1, the secret white-walled compound Hu himself had set up amid fruit orchards no more than twenty-five miles from where the two of them now sat talking to each other. There, in the soundless cells, the ideological losers of the last great game were "reeducated." It was difficult, now, for the American to picture the smooth-faced, smiling man seated across from him constrained in a "peace suit," a rubber uniform, being reeducated.

Mr. Hu smiled too, then took up again the chain of cigarettes which he had started smoking in 1936 at the age of thirteen when, as a Communist militant, he descended into the old Peking underground with his terrorist cadre. The diminutive Mr. Hu, at sixty-one, could pass for forty; his small hands were almost delicate, and his round face was unlined, the hair jet black. At the age of thirteen he could and did pass for a nine-year-old walking down the street with his parents, so that when they laid a bomb or cut an informer's throat no one ever suspected the sweet-looking boy in the short pants with the bangs covering his forehead. By the time of the Long March, in the 1940s, Hu was a ferocious fighter and a gifted strategist, and he won the approbation of Mao himself after the first great "encirclement campaign."

Mr. Hu had long been the master of what was called the Zig-Zag by the cadre; he had managed to walk the tightrope of the Cultural Revolution, only falling, temporarily, after the assassination of Lin Pao and the rise of the Gang of Four in the early '70s. By 1980, Ding Xiaoping had purged in his turn the remaining Maoists who had, three times, imprisoned him. A new niche had been carved in 1981 for Mr. Hu: Head, Standing Committee of the Party Secretariat. In this capacity Mr. Hu was charged with (in fact conceived of) the policy of putting an end to the public meetings, the wall posters of criticism and the constitutional guarantees that had been in use for two years. Mr. Hu, according to U.S. Intelligence estimates, was a hard hardliner. The fact, by itself, that it was he who was meeting with the American representative, was enough to send a shiver down the spine of the diplomatic world.

Wolf could not help but admire this survivor of the Japanese, Chiang Kai-shek, the Americans, the "Capitalist Roaders," and, finally, the Gang of Four. It was said that Mr. Hu's young bride had been one of those boiled alive by Chiang's Kuomintang torturers. In the midst of the new leadership that had succeeded to 1982, Mr. Hu stood out like a poisonous and tough old medicine tree in a set garden.

Mr. Hu leaned back and rubbed his round head as if to generate energy. He was laughing about something. Wolf smiled and tried to get a focus on the fierce little man . . . "The wood, ah, yes, of course. Superb."

The two men, almost comically at odds with each other in physical terms, sipped their warm sweetened tea and admired the antique gleam of the den's wood floor and appointments. Mr. Hu's English was correct and almost uninflected, not unlike Manheim's own speech pattern, and the small man's voice was unexpectedly deep. "Dr. Manheim, do you know this dish of the grasslands region? . . ."

The diminishing influx of daylight bounced gently off the canvases and carvings that looked out at the American visitor in this den. Above Mr. Hu's chaise Wolf recognized and admired out loud a superb rendering of Mi Fu bowing to a stone. To the American this painting summed up the hidden reality of the Chinese. Mi Fu was a legendary eleventh-century diplomat who had come to pay his respects to the royal court. The wise visitor first insisted on rendering homage to a nearby rock famous for its fantastic shape.

As if reading Wolf's thoughts, Mr. Hu commented, "Those were different diplomats, doctor, they renounced their power over the world of nature in order to remain in communion with it, while we pulverize her to make energy. In your country young people study Zen and the aesthetics of the ancient dynasties—here Hegel and Marx have conquered the phenomenological world." He grunted and lit another Lucky Strike.

Wolf thought, but did not say, No, we do not now bow down before a tree or a stone. When we see a stone polished smooth by the winds, or the roots of a tree crawling along the earth, we diplomats of today turn away. He was beginning to think like B.J.; he could see her as she had been—poised on the sand two nights before in Hawaii—as he stared at the cloud-capped mountains in another of Mr. Wong's Song dynasty paintings. Uncanny how like the thunderheads over Waikiki they were.

To the Chinese, Wolf knew, each work of art was imbued with *qi,* the invisible yet profound energy binding nature to a work of art that imitates it. The Chinese had built up an aesthetic tradition, based on nature, unrivaled in the history of civilization, and now the marketing zeal of the big corporations was choking China with Western consumer goods. Wolf agreed with B.J. that this was arrogant and would, in the Chinese way of thinking, somehow bring bad luck to both countries.

Mr. Hu broke the tall American's reverie with a poem fragment from Wang Wei, a painter from the Tang dynasty:

> *You ask what is the ultimate word*
> *of philosophy?*
> *The answer lies in the song of the*
> *fishermen returning to shore*

In less than ten minutes the verbal preliminaries were nearly over. The teacups stood empty. The cold winter light had begun to fail by midmorning, yet no lamp was turned on in the den to relieve the chiaroscuro as the two men sat at modified right angles to each other in their high-backed chairs—from what dynasty the American could no longer afford to wonder as his mind scrambled to sort out the new ground rules of this unique meeting.

Vis-à-vis, they were alone in a setting of virtual conspiracy rather than of statecraft. The meeting of just the two would flash across the media of the entire world and, certainly, drive the Soviets further into a frenzy.

The PRC Politburo, especially Mr. Hu, seemed to have a genius for maddening Moscow. It had been, in part, Mr. Hu's machinations in 1979 that had helped rationalize the Soviets slashing into Afghanistan. Indeed, it was said that Mr. Hu and Dr. Manheim together had convinced General Gia, dictator of Pakistan, to allow U.S. and PRC advisers and material to reach Afghan rebels through the Western corridor of his country. That was past now, and prologue, and the two men were once again working together.

Each knew all that they could about the other, and there was mutual admiration and respect. Mr. Hu believed that the experience of the concentration camp had made Dr. Manheim into a mature and serious statesman, much more so, he thought, than either Drs. Kissinger or Brzezinski. Those two, Mr. Hu was convinced, had been products of the European experience and of World War II. It was possible to talk to them, but he found them, unlike Manheim, both vain and shallow because they had not suffered sufficiently. Only Manheim had suffered, as Hu had, as a child.

For his part, Wolf was a student of the Long March of the Chinese to revolution. Mr. Hu was everywhere celebrated in story and ballet as the youngest hero of that epic still living. The American liked nothing more than hearing memories of men like Mr. Hu, and this had helped their relationship grow.

The young men of the revolutionary army all had nicknames, and young Hu's was the "Old Dog." He had marched more than two thousand miles to join the revolutionary Army. His mother and father had been killed in one of Chiang Kai-shek's White air force bombing raids against Nanking. All these boys had known much suffering, yet that was in their past. In 1979 Mr. Hu, remembering these "days of rebirth" to Wolf Manheim, had recalled for him the watchword of the revolutionary army—"We will shoot our way into history"—and together they had hummed a few bars of "The East Is Red" and toasted, privately, the new U.S.-PRC pact. It had never been necessary for either man to comment on the radical differences and similarities between their two boyhoods . . . between the Long March and Buchenwald.

Being fired in the kiln of the Long March must, Wolf believed, somehow have rendered Hu immune to the constant disequilibrium of Chinese politics since the revolution. He only half-listened to Mr. Hu, now, as he talked about the coming snowstorm while Wolf marveled that anyone could have survived those zigs and zags of the decade 1966–1976. Mr. Hu was the only man left in the Politburo who had actually survived the political *and* the Cultural

Revolution . . . and its aftermath.

The infighting over who or who had not "conspired with the Gang of Four" was still growing ever more intense, setting Washington's teeth on edge. Because any Soviet threats against the PRC were fraught with danger, Wolf had argued the instability of the Chinese leadership to the cabinet. Mr. Hu was the only remaining link left between the antiradicals in power and the thousands of radicals out of power who were appalled and infuriated by the "capitalist road" that they believed the PRC was now following to hell.

Under the banner of "Modernization," the radicals believed, the new "open heart" policy of the regime was nothing but a modern version of the hated "Open Door" policy of eighty-five years ago when America and the European powers had looted the old China and afflicted their children by expanding the opium trade. Now, once again, the Beijing Hotel was aswarm with traders from the West. In the streets, instead of the red slogans of Mao, were billboards advertising hairstyling shampoo for women—in the Occidental style—"vanishing" cream, cashmere sweaters, leisure and sporting toys and clothes. This "Coca-Colazation," as they called it, of their sacred revolution had set in motion a deep reaction among Communist Party cadre, intellectuals and students, many of whom looked to Mr. Hu to lead a coup against the "modernists". Should this happen, Wolf had insisted in Washington and to NATO, the Soviets would be sorely tempted to make their move.

"Fusang," Wolf heard Mr. Hu say, then chuckle through the cigarette smoke. The first time that the two of them had ever met, in Islamabad in 1979, Mr. Hu had tested him with the story of how an ancient Buddhist monk named Huishen ("a direct ancestor," claimed Mr. Hu, straightfaced) had led a religious party to Palos Verdes, on the coast of southern California. "And this, Dr. Manheim, was in the year 452!"

"452? What calendar—"

"452 A.D.! Five hundred years before the Vikings, a thousand before Columbus." Then had followed a fascinating and utterly political digression. This fable, told by Mr. Hu, in 1979, was sufficient to strike up a fateful relationship that now, five years later, could change history in reality, as the story did rhetorically.

Then as now they had been sitting alone in the hot honeymoon suite of the Islamabad Hilton. Wolf had drunk iced tea and listened while Mr. Hu rested his case on the detailed accounts of marriage customs, crime and slavery that Huishen brought back from Fusang—descriptions which tallied almost exactly with what had been learned about fifth-century Mexican society. Furthermore, the fusang tree, the sacred tree for which Huishen said the local people of that era named the country, appeared to be the cactuslike agave common throughout Mexico. As to whether ancient Chinese ships were capable of transpacific voyages, Mr. Hu, a maritime historian, had no doubts.

"For long periods, China led the ancient world in navigation," he said. "As early as the fourth century B.C., her ships plied the neighboring seas . . . and entered the Pacific beyond . . . In the first century A.D. the Chinese already knew how to use the sternpost rudder to keep ships on course. China was also prosperous enough to finance such explorations. One third-century Chinese kingdom, the Wu, had a navy of five thousand ships, the largest with several decks and enough berths for three thousand passengers. Voyages to the Philippines and other South China seaports were commonplace even before the birth of Christ."

Not content with besting Columbus and Leif Ericsson, Hu had also hypothesized that fifteen hundred years *before* Huishen set off for Fusang, Chinese seafarers may have come up with another prize find: California. "American archeologists at the University of San Diego discovered stone anchors off the California coast that are about three thousand years old and Asian in origin. Such discoveries provide solid scientific evidence of Chinese transpacific voyages in pre-Colombian times and add support to the theory that the ancient cultures of the Americas have been . . . influenced by ideas of Chinese origin."

Wolf had searched the round face, under its halo of yellow cigarette smoke. Dare he point out that he was familiar with a long article by Mr. Hu entitled "Columbus the Colonial Pirate" wherein the author rehearsed the vintage grudge against the Italian brigand who had originally set out to plunder Asia?

Instead, Mr. Hu had politely glossed over Columbus's expansionist tendencies and instead called for further searches for relics along the California coast that he said "may well turn up more evidence of friendly intercourse between China and the Americas in ancient times."

Wolf had understood. The China Card was a reality at last.

Now, five years later, Mr. Hu appeared ready to play it.

Mr. Hu was just stubbing out one cigarette and lighting another when he signaled to Wolf (by quoting from a poem by Mao) that the first phase of the preliminaries was over. Nevertheless, as Wolf was aware, Chinese love to discuss the weather and count themselves masters at predicting when storms will arrive or heat waves end, all based on the old Chinese lunar calendar.

" 'Over Chungshan swept a storm, headlong'—you know it, Dr. Manheim?"

"I'm not sure. Didn't the Chairman write it after the fall of Nanking?"

"Exactly. After the *liberation* of Nanking, in 1949. '. . . Our mighty army, a million strong, has crossed the Great River . . .

>The City, a tiger crouching, a dragon curling,
>   outshines its ancient glories;
>A heroic triumph heaven and earth have been
>   overturned . . .

> Where Nature sentient, she too would pass from
>   youth to age,
> But man's world is mutable, seas become mulberry
>   fields' . . .

Things seemed much simpler then, somehow."

Wolf nodded with emphasis, waited. Mr. Hu rose and turned on a single red-shaded lamp. The Tang dynasty wood and the objects, carved before Marco Polo's time, gave off a dull glow. Wolf sat with the window and the leaden sky behind him, his face and hair in silhouette. Mr. Hu had disappeared into a shadow at the far corner of the French Empire sofa. The tip of his always-burning cigarette danced about in the shadow as if he were signaling to the American on some level much more basic than that of diplomatic rhetoric. In fact, Wolf understood that he would be required to discover meaning at multiple levels during this meeting, both from what was said as well as from what went unsaid, beginning with the fact that they were meeting without an interpreter. Surely the selection of Mr. Hu to meet *alone* with the American presidential representative was a dramatic gesture, meant for home consumption, to pacify the party's left wing . . . So Wolf watched and waited.

"I believe," murmured Mr. Hu, "that Soviet Russia is preparing to make an 'incursion' into the People's Republic of China, and that unless the United States of America takes certain steps, world war will follow logically."

The cigarette ember glowed and faded. Wolf sat immobile . . . "Mr. Vice-Chairman, I am here to listen to you. I think that we know each other well enough for you to be certain that I will convey your wishes directly, and in confidence, to the White House." Mr. Hu struck a match and sighed and then began again in a firmer but still quiet tone.

"I say that the Soviet Union is preparing for war. I base this on combined intelligence and common sense—it would be evident

even if the ultimatums were not flying back and forth in the headlines . . . Though inferior to you in terms of nuclear weapons, the
Soviets now hold both military and naval strategic superiority. I see
that you do not waste time in disagreement with that basic reality.
But because the U.S. now realizes the extent of Soviet hegemony
and appetites, she and her NATO allies have begun a belated effort
to arrive at strategic parity. This goal is, unfortunately, still perhaps
five years away—a window of time during which the Soviets reason
that they can complete their design of hegemony against the People's Republic of China, consolidate territorial gains and then—and
only then, from strength—commence once again to clamor for
nuclear disarmament."

Wolf recrossed his legs and rubbed the cleft in his chin. The
silence required some response. "You discount the new U.S. laser
weaponry?"

"Only for two more years, Mr. Ambassador, but even that will
come too late. By that time our new industrial complexes along the
border with Soviet Russia will have been overrun and demolished.
By that time, who knows what twists and turns will have taken
place within the People's Republic. Will not the world say, China
boasts a population in excess of one billion, what difference do a few
million more or less matter—"

"A *few* million?"

"Yes. I am not speaking about a Soviet nuclear attack. And no
one can *occupy* China. I am talking about a conventional invasion.
They will bite off Sinkiang and the outlying provinces, capture
undeveloped oil and mineral resources, and crowd hundreds of
millions of our people into the eastern provinces, crippling us for
generations."

"But Mr. Vice-Chairman, for the last two weeks your public
statements have, without exception, been couched in terms of nuclear war, have they not?"

"Mr. Ambassador, what choice have we? If the Soviets attack us with conventional weapons only—as they will—China would have *no* allies in this hemisphere. The Soviets, however, have the best fighting army in the world in the Vietnamese, who are—I say it between us—ready to launch a devastating second front against all contiguous borders."

"And yet, Mr. Hu, do we not face the danger of Soviet overreaction to what they insist on calling America's China Card? Because, as you once said, the leverage of the U.S.-PRC alliance rests on the card being held *but not being played.* If we announce that we are activating a Chinese-American-Japanese alliance (the 'new axis' as the Soviets say), can we be sure that the USSR will not launch a preemptive strike while China is still weak?"

"Sir, there are now elements in China that favor a rapprochement with the Soviet Union. Did you know that? That would be the end for you, of course. That is why we are meeting, and that is why I must come out of this meeting with a weapon that can be used to crush these revisionists."

Wolf shifted and Mr. Hu seemed to understand that the American needed to use the water closet as well as to absorb what had been spoken thus far. When he returned Wolf saw that it had begun to snow, just as Mr. Hu had said it would. It made the small Politburo member's geopolitical predictions all the more chilling, and Wolf felt the band tighten across his temples.

"Mr. Vice-Chairman, the Soviets know that you have begun to evacuate key areas, that you have deployed surface-to-air missiles, that you have a new generation of weapons systems provided by both the United States and Japan—"

"Mr. Ambassador, compared to them we have *nothing.* If we use a single nuclear weapon they will eliminate our every facility— *permanently*—knowing that the world will do nothing because China will be branded as the first nation to use nuclear weapons . . . since Hiroshima. No, the Soviets are praying for us to use them, so that they can '*re*act.' "

"You make the worst case, in terms of the PRC."

"Mr. Ambassador, if I am overstating the case, then why are a million Soviet troops massing on our border? Why is most of the Soviet Pacific nuclear submarine fleet at this moment in the South China Sea? You're not surprised at that, surely? Perhaps you didn't think *we* knew? Oh, yes, carrying cruise-type missiles, patroling within reach of the Strait of Malacca . . ."

Wolf had heard it all before. One of the chief reasons that the PRC had insisted on talking with him instead of the hawkish Secretary of State Higgins was that he, Wolf, more nearly understood how the Chinese felt about the Soviet Union. During their meetings in the days of the Afghanistan invasion, Mr. Hu had confided to the American what Wolf, alone, of the National Security Council, had suspected: It had been Mao Tse-tung, above all others, who had made the historic decision to reject the USSR and embrace the USA.

"Chairman Mao," Mr. Hu had said, "always took the long view of history. In that view, he believed, the United States would prevail over the Soviet Union. The Chairman used to say that they, the Russians, had no *renaissance; sauvage,* he called them. 'Only their military works,' he used to say."

Then Mr. Hu told Wolf that in the bad old days in Imperial China petty criminals were forced to join the army and spend the rest of their lives in distant military outposts, so that the Chinese now hated the regular military. And when they looked across their border at the USSR that was all they saw—the military behemoth. Russia equaled Japan of the 1930s. Except that the PRC had demanded that Japan rearm in order to face Soviet drive for hegemony. A nuclear Japanese fleet was to be the PRC's Japanese Card. So much for equation of power, counter-power.

When Richard Nixon and Henry Kissinger first came to China in 1972, their mouths hung open when Mao, and then Chou, told them "You will *win.* We have known that since the start of the

Great Cultural Revolution." All this and more Wolf had learned from Mr. Hu. For now it was only required of him that he sit and listen to variations on the theme.

"Did they not transfer more than one-third of their Warsaw Pact forces from Eastern Europe to our border? Why have the Soviets worked around the clock to complete new mail and truck routes to Siberia? And, above all, why have they chosen to honor their mutual defense treaties with the Vietnamese against Thailand and ourselves?" The man must stop smoking sometime; the American could no longer see Mr. Hu behind the cloud of smoke.

"Mr. Vice-Chairman, can you be saying that China is lost unless the threat of war is escalated to the nuclear level, because China is at the mercy, strategically, of the Soviet Union?"

"Because we are *both* at their mercy, Mr. Ambassador." He had stopped smoking.

"That's as it may be, but my question is how a nuclear war could 'save' the Chinese people."

"Not a nuclear war, Mr. Ambassador, the *threat* of a nuclear war . . . an ultimatum *from the United States to the Soviet Union.*"

He could dimly hear voices beyond the door, perhaps the reporters' luncheon had already begun. "Mr. Hu, in all candor, the NATO alliance would climb the wall. Surely, we two must also discuss the other option—negotiations."

The little man rose and emptied the round stone ashtray, then stood holding the heavy object in his hand. His Mao uniform was, after the fashion, too large for his small frame, and his rimless glasses had slipped a bit down onto his flat nose, yet he was, as he stood there, Wolf knew, one of the most determined and important men in the world at that moment. The vice-chairman's voice, when he spoke, was halfway between a hiss and a whisper.

"Dr. Manheim. There *is* no negotiation with Russian expansionism that has had China as its target since the fourteenth century. Everyone knows that Russia—old and new—has been cannibalizing China: in the Pomer area twenty thousand square hectares, more than six hundred vital islands, the entire South China Sea, the oil shelf from the Strait of Korea to Southeast Asia, altogether more than five million square hectares of Chinese territory. The Chinese people are once again completely encircled and once again, let me assure you, *we will break out.*" He set the ashtray down suddenly on the inlaid end table and adjusted his glasses, then stared out into the storm as if seeing once again the blood on the ice as the Eighth Route Army fought hand to hand in the snow against Chiang Kai-shek.

"An ultimatum from the United States, sir, will have the support of the industrial nations of the Second World as well as the poor peoples of the Third World because *every one of them* is equally threatened by the same Soviet expansionism." He continued to stare, past Wolf's shoulder, out into the storm . . .

"Mr. Hu, you believe that a U. S. threat *alone,* would be sufficient? Remembering that after Afghanistan the United States stationed a *permanent* aircraft-carrier task force in the Indian Ocean. That we have now—in fact as of 1983—set up joint naval bases with the British at Diego Garcia, as well as military installations in Oman, Kenya, Somalia, Egypt and, of course, Israel. We have suffered serious domestic turmoil because of registration and draft laws and the expense of a multi-billion-dollar rapid deployment force. Despite tremendous pressure our economic sanctions against Russia are still in place, and though this is an election year, we are going to put billions more into the MX missile crash program. I say all this, Mr. Vice-Chairman, because the President is most concerned that you realize that the United States is in no way quitting on its agreements with the People's Republic. You are a shrewd observer, sir, you certainly know that domestic problems could tear our nation apart . . . our economy is teetering on the edge of a 1929 situation, and yet despite everything we have matched the Soviets across the board in terms of conventional air- and sea-lift capabilities for projecting forces into distant areas to the point where we now face the probability of a direct confrontation between U. S. and USSR forces—"

In Chinese, softly as if to himself, Mr. Hu interrupted with, "Either the East Wind prevails over the West Wind or . . ." His fierce eyes behind his polished lenses were as slate gray as the winter sky, his thoughts going back to the time of his youth, and the Long March when nothing had been impossible and they had sung their battle songs as they marched across China, a distance of 6,000 *li,* and picked and ate the wild apricots. They had broken out of each encirclement by the enemy. Infuriated by the revolutionaries' escape from his "Fifth Encirclement" campaign, Generalissimo Chiang Kai-shek had mobilized fresh forces to block the Communist vanguard from crossing the strategic river of Tatu. Failure to cross the Tatu meant that the momentum of the long march would be broken, and with it almost any chance of ultimate success. This was do or die and Mao knew it. With what looked to the world like almost superhuman will the Red Army cut north from the Yangtze into the province of Szechuan, then into the dreaded tribal lands of the ferocious aborigines, the "White" and "Black" Lolos of Lololand.

Though never conquered and living only to kill Chinese, the Lolo chieftains were brought to understand that the Red Chinese and the Black Lolos should combine to destroy Chiang's Nationalist forces. Guns changed hands and Mao's forces were speeding toward the Tatu.

Led by aborigine guides, Hu's vanguard crept though the unexplored forests of Lololand, unseen by Chiang's airplanes. Hu and his comrades crawled ahead to climb ancient trees and spy down on the village of An Jen Ch'ang. Peering down from the heights, the scouts saw that Chiang's general staff—never dreaming that the opposition had penetrated Lololand—had gone off to a feast and left behind three ferryboats on the south side of the river. Mr. Hu could recall decades later the feel of the bark on the palms of his hands, the ants crawling over his arms as he hung suspended in the giant black hardwood tree. That crossing had been both an historical and personal rite of passage. None of the men of Tatu could ever cross back over, they were all on the far side of history now . . .

Their eyes met almost on a level even though Mr. Hu was standing and the tall American was sitting. Mr. Hu's fingers twitched at his sides as he pronounced what was clearly his final word. Each phrase was as measured and hard as a weapon of war.

"Mr. Manheim, there is, we know, a policy in Washington known as the Guam Doctrine whereby the United States does everything within its power to see that its allies do everything within *their* powers to defend U.S. interests. We know this, and certainly the members of NATO know this. They know that the U.S. is, as we say, a real tiger *and* a paper tiger. That is why Mr. Strauss of Germany has been so helpful to us—that great statesman." His face betrayed no irony. "To the Germans, the 'Red' danger of the USSR is more threatening than the 'yellow' of the PRC. The French and British feel this way too. Because of this, we now have the Harrier jump-jets, the Trousal and Alouette transports and helicopters, and what you may not have known is that we have secured Crolate ground-to-air missiles and Exocet ship-to-ship missiles. In short, the NATO countries know that the PRC is the 'sixteenth member' of the North Atlantic bloc . . . Thanks to you, sir, we have the basis of a neutron bomb system. Besides, we have doubled the size of our nuclear submarine fleet; this you must have known . . . Now you say that the Soviets may challenge your ultimatum, but the real probabilities are that they will not. On the other hand, if you remain silent in the face of our actions to defend ourselves—in Mongolia, Thailand, Kampuchea, Vietnam—then we *will* be forced to use our nuclear arsenal, such as it is. And we will thus bring all of Europe into the theater of hostilities. Then, and you cannot deny it, the United States will be isolated by geographical distance and forced to use its *strategic* weapons. You Americans have no system of shelters as we do, and unlike the Soviet shelter system, ours *works.* What I wrote in 1982, I meant —'In the theory of the three worlds we comprehend world war. The peoples of the Third World will have broad opportunities to organize war against aggression'—"

Wolf was compelled to add, "And I believe, Mr. Hu, that your essay concluded that, 'after a protracted joint effort, the peoples of the world will finally destroy the warmongers.' We were never sure whom exactly you had in mind besides the Soviets, if anyone. Then you also concluded that you believed that our estimate of 400 million casualties in a limited nuclear war to be inaccurate, that any such war would lead to deaths of over two *billion* . . . Please forgive me for interrupting, Mr. Vice-Chairman, but I want you to know that I am following you closely, that I am understanding you. In other words, that we are your friends."

"Sir, I do not doubt it. But we are saying to you, as Israel said privately to you, 'We will not go down alone.' You have made your position clear on Israel. We are now asking for you to make yourselves clear on the matter of the one billion Chinese . . . I am referring now to certain understandings that go back to Mr. John Dulles and his brother Mr. Allen Dulles, later to Mr. Rusk and Mr. Kissinger and Mr. Brzezinski and down to this day and this hour and to you, Dr. Manheim."

The American representative stood up. Hu stepped to his elbow as if to lead him into the state luncheon that waited. Wolf listened for the final word.

"You know we have a story from the *Huai nan Tzu:* In ancient times Kungkung and Chaunsu fought each other for the throne. In a fit of rage Kungkung bulled against Mount Anchou, breaking the pillars of heaven and snapping the ties of the earth. Then the sky shifted towards the northwest, tilting the sun, moon and stars;

while in the southeast the earth sank so that dirt and water gathered there."

Mr. Hu looked up at the American with something new in his eyes that Wolf could not comprehend at once, then Mr. Hu moved to the door to open it for his guest. "Come," he said, "it is time for the toasts." But neither man moved. The words of Hu's story seemed to reverberate in the ancient room (". . . in a fit of rage . . . breaking the pillars . . . snapping the ties . . .")

The band tightened across the American's forehead, his skull began to tingle. A fit of rage, he thought, that goes all the way back, to Mr. John Foster Dulles and his brother Allen . . .

BEIJING AGAIN PLAYS HOLE CARD IN STRATEGIC POKER
(A SPECIAL ESSAY FROM OUR CORRESPONDENT)
BY
Betsy Jones-Russell

The advanced intercontinental ballistic missile that China fired some 6,000 miles into the Pacific on October 18, 1983, sent lasting waves of turbulence rippling through superpower relationships. On each of the three previous occasions when China made major strategic moves, the complexion of international relations was radically altered, according to a high White House source.

The first occasion was the nuclear sharing agreement between China and the Soviet Union in October 1957, immediately after the Soviet's first successful ICBM launch.

The second Chinese nuclear scare came in October 1964, when Beijing exploded its first atomic device. This time the Chinese action alarmed the Russians as much as the Americans, deepening the Sino-Soviet split into a chasm.

The third Chinese strategic weapon breakthrough to shake up superpower relations came in 1970—the satellite, making it a point to note that it passed over both Moscow and Washington.

U.S. hardliners will no doubt interpret the Chinese ballistic launch last October as a significant payoff on the so-called "China Card" strategy—the effort by national security adviser Wolfgang Manheim to line up Beijing with Washington against the Soviet Union.

Why now? There is good evidence that the Chinese only make major moves in the strategic field if they believe the time and opportunity are right. All of the previous strategic moves occurred in times of international

141

tensions, when it served China to send out warnings to either or both of the superpowers that Beijing was a force to reckon with.

This is true today. Beijing apparently perceives its top-secret arms deal with the United States as nearly a blank check to use against "Soviet aggression," according to high-ranking PRC officials. The present crisis is being fueled by rumors that this secret Chinese Card is being played by Wolfgang Manheim and much of the U.S. foreign establishment. Thus, the advanced Chinese missile fired into the South Pacific in 1983 served notice on Moscow that China is no longer merely a regional power, but is now the third-ranking member of the ICBM club, and an American partner.

Past evidence suggests that the present military crisis—now primarily in the Middle East and Southeast Asia—can be expected to worsen. . . .

12

THE FORBIDDEN CITY—
JANUARY 23, 1984
(MONDAY)

They walked toward the ancient gates of the Forbidden City as if they were heroes in a Chinese opera with thousands of supernumeraries swirling around them. "Whither China?" she said and, "Wolf, have you been in the city *under* this—dug out in case of nuclear war?"

He waved rather self-consciously to the applauding crowd and talked to her through unmoving lips. "How did you get that statement by Hu?"

"What statement?"

"What statement! The goddamn World-War-III-is-inevitable story that you—"

"Uh, language, doctor, language. Mr. Hu was the epitome of revolutionary chivalry and quite happy to speak to me for a few moments . . ."

"Chivalry? You don't mean, you can't mean that just to score a beat on the world press that you'd—"

"Oh, shut up, you chauvinist swine. I look on Mr. Hu as a grandfather figure . . . It's *you* who won't say a word about your meeting. Stop trying to distract me with gossip. What took place?

"On the plane," he smiled to the crowd, and not at her, "later."

"We can't go on meeting like this," she said as Jarrell's Secret Service team cleared the people to the sides so that the two of them could walk through the high red-stone walls into Chunanhai, the Forbidden City. "The world press is going to *just* tolerate the SS keeping them back like this because they know that your commitment to these interviews predates the crisis, *and* if you give me something about your meeting with Hu to give to *them* . . ."

Huge colored photo-paintings of Lenin marked the entrance into the Forbidden City. In the near distance the many-colored tiers of the ancient palace sparkled in the clear, sun-filled air of a classic Beijing winter day. The wind was down, the temperature had shot up into the low 50s and the sun was so warm and bright that both had borrowed dark glasses from the Secret Service. Both wore bulky layers of quilted greatcoats; the major networks would televise Wolf Manheim tonight and speculate about what message he was bringing back to the President, while the world waited.

They were past the entrance now and into the vast square, the American and Chinese plainclothes security edging back the curious crowds and equipment-laden media people. Security maintained a space, like a stage, of some fifty feet all around them so they could talk and breathe in the clear air. Yesterday's snow was melting off, but underneath the arches and on the ancient steps on the shadowy side of the square, the leavings from the storm were a clean white that would linger for a few more hours. Neither the willows demarking the canal nor their wavy reflections could be seen from where they walked, only the bare-branched tops black against the sky.

"These cobblestones are marvelous," she said; and, "Look at the blue filigree pattern on that pagoda. Extraordinary. There was a United States senator at the turn of the century who announced 'With God's help, we shall raise Shanghai up and up and up until it reaches the level of Kansas City. It's true. China, that was the ultimate in pottery, food, eroticism and—"

"Landscape painting," he said. "These sunglasses really help. Be careful of people in the crowd who can lip-read. There mustn't be any leaks before I talk to the President; that means cutting out the KGB and the CIA, let alone the media."

"Then you have to give me something for them, Wolf."

"I will. I'll make something up later . . . It's hard to be away from you at night . . . I miss you."

"I know. I miss you. I dream about you. Last night you were a black stallion and I was, ah, riding you."

"With those glasses on I can't tell if you're having me on. Is that the phrase?"

"Depends . . . Did you know that B.R. was here more than sixty years ago?"

"No."

"Oh yes. He wrote about its 'ancient beauty' and he loved the people. As much as he was allergic to Russia, he was fascinated by China. He sailed from Marseilles with his mistress—the Chinese were *not* scandalized, by the way—on the Red Sea route, stopped in Saigon. The Europeans, he said, were all enormously rich and very ill—the women driving through the street crowds in limousines, gorgeously dressed, rouged, but with hollow cheeks and all suggesting death."

"Tell me more about B.R. in China, this may be the last sane conversation in private, or in public, that we can look forward to for some time." He waved again, to the left and right. She luxuriated in the crispness of the day, so unexpected, so changed.

"Well, the British Foreign Office was, of course, paranoid about what he would say while he was here, so, according to the record, as soon as B.R. arrived he was made number six on a list of spies, murderers and other disreputable types categorized as 'Suspected Persons.' They were as incensed about his traveling with his mistress as they were about his Fabian socialism and antiestablishmentarian sentiments. At any rate, the visit was a triumph. His lectures on philosophy at the old Peking University were packed. Both Chou En-lai and Mao Tse-tung attended . . . In those days it was called Peiping, wasn't it? . . ."

They paused to take in the sweep of the ancient city. The onlookers were thinning out and some of the press trailed away to check out of the Beijing Hotel and encamp at the airport in preparation for Air Force Two's 5:00 P.M. departure. A number of others trooped off to look at the tomb of Chairman Mao just outside the gates. The sun was climbing; the last of the snow beginning to melt; all over Red Square classes of schoolchildren bundled in quilted blue and gray kept pace with teachers. "Aren't they gorgeous?" she said. "You don't have any children anywhere, do you?"

"Not that I know of. You?"

"No—and I'm positive. I was going to wait until I was thirty-five. That will pass this summer . . ."

"It's not too late, is it?" A troop of five- and six-year-olds passed, staring, the baby-skin red and brown hues of their faces glowing in the cold. "Look at them," she said. "The gene pool . . . I don't know, Wolf. I used to think that I'd marry first. Then I decided I would pick a sire and raise the offspring myself. I just don't know."

"You can't let the Russell genes burn out."

"What about the Manheim genes? Are you the last of the line, forever the world's most eligible bachelor? You were an only child?"

"Yes. My mother died when I was seven. She was not Jewish . . . she was an anthropologist." Betsy tried to see through his dark glasses. In one phrase, for an instant, again, he had seemed open with her and vulnerable. She wanted to touch him but instead, out of the corner of her eye, she caught the image of James Jarrell, a thin wire running down from his ear and disappearing into his coat, staring at her.

"B. R. nearly died here," she said. "Yes, it's quite true. They were going to bury him on an island, the Western Lake, and make a god of him. He was delirious for days. As soon as he'd recovered slightly he set out for home, in a rage to live . . ."

Near the canal a line of old people were shadowboxing and bending deliberately in the Tai Chi Chuan exercises. As they swayed they exhaled a kind of wailing cough that echoed off the water and across Red Square. Oh, God, she wanted to say out loud, I want to have a baby with you. But they stood rooted, listening as the cries of the old people rang off the canals and the cobblestones and, it seemed, the vault of the winter sky. Then she smelled the aroma of a street vendor's stand of hot wonton, long and twisted and wrapped in tissue paper. Pungent, mouth-watering—never had she felt life so exquisitely, every sense was awake; the cries from the canal, the unexpected colors of the pagodas, the rich smell from the food stand. It was as if all the stimuli combined suddenly, so that she blurted—"Wolf, I want to . . ."

"What?" he said.

"I don't know . . . walk." She had started to say "make a child with you," then had decided, midphrase, to shift to "make love with you," but Jarrell's presence had made her stop altogether. They began to walk again, slowly. In a few months, she mused, the fine yellow dust could cover the entire square. Will any of it filter down into the underground city? Will I be with child? Under the on-slaught of stimuli and sensation, from both sides of her skin, she already felt she was, somehow, pregnant with life. "It's warm like New York in early April. Did you know that the Chinese don't perspire?"

"Yes. They lack the glands. To them we smell rank." He unbuttoned his coat. "*Tienchi hen hao.* It is hot today. They are especially offended by perfume. You smell good, to me."

"I'm horny, Wolf, and hungry, and happy."

"I want you right here in the street," he kept his lips compressed, his voice a suppressed hum.

It looked to the bystanders as if the two tall people had thrown back their heads and laughed for no reason, since it seemed that they had not even been talking.

"Wolf, you're showing me more of yourself than before . . . even in bed," she said through tight lips.

"Maybe it's the war scare. You have to trust somebody."

They turned and started back toward the gates. Bicycle bells punctuated the still almost empty spaces of Red Square. By the canals the old people still spoke out in their slow, balletic shadowboxing.

"Those old people. The sound they make. Shadowboxing like that. Wolf, did you get anywhere yesterday? You know, you're the man. This is not 1962, there's no B.R. to cable Krushchev and Kennedy to stand back from the brink. There just aren't any men any more with the moral authority of a Russell or an Einstein to say 'This cannot be.' "

They walked slowly, silently, each lost in thought. The high nasal cries of the shadowboxers echoed across Red Square. Under their feet was another city, a double for this one, a place to flee from radioactive rain and lightning. Out loud, she said, "The Forbidden City under the Forbidden City."

"Watch out for the lip-readers," he said with no smile.

She thought to herself, I'm getting a bit like ma—looking for heroes. Wolf Manheim looks like a great man, but is he? There's no question that the U.S. can intervene—not dictate but intervene —if Wolf will sell it to the President. Remembering her mother's scorn for the statesmen of her time, of how Britain did not do anything to strengthen peace or stop war . . .

"We have to go to the mausoleum to pay our respects to Chairman Mao," he spoke in a normal tone.

"You know," she spoke in a normal tone now, too, "my mother was crazy, I told you that, but she wasn't *that* crazy. When General Millan's men screamed out '*Viva la Muerte!*' at the University of Salamanca, Unamuno stood up and told them that their cry 'Long Live Death!' was necrophilia—"

"They killed him while he was under house arrest, didn't they?"

"Yes. Like Neruda or Lorca. So?"

"So? Because Bertrand Russell couldn't stop World War I by going to jail, or Unamuno the Spanish Civil War by confronting the Fascists. It isn't enough."

"What *is* enough? You were in Buchenwald, you of all people know that a handful exterminated millions—"

"*Please* keep your voice down." A donkey-drawn cart rattled past and then there were more flower-faced children. The oversize poster paintings of Lenin were behind them and the mausoleum with its giant portrait of Mao hanging from outer columns was in front and to their left. The crowds were beginning to form around their circle of space again, and the always-present queue waiting for a look into the glass coffin wound around toward the bottom of the square. "Another great man, another mythomaniac," she said.

"What? Who, Mao?" He took off the dark glasses.

"They all create their own myths, these historical figures, they use up millions of other people in their mythomania." The crowd was growing, and cameramen were setting up to get a visual of the U.S. representative as he entered the tomb.

"Oh, yes, you're center stage in this well-made drama. But when the curtain falls do all you famous men descend together into the nether world under our feet, into that perpetual gloom?"

"B.S., B.J.," he bit out, "not now. Save it."

Jarrell and his lead-man shouldered a wedge for the VIP to enter the tomb ahead of the long line of people, four abreast, who had been waiting since early morning. The crowd seemed not to mind, even applauding, while whole classes of schoolchildren waved their little red flags vigorously.

Inside was silence, muted light and a wending line of visitors looking into the glass coffin at the Great Teacher. The tomb was in the Greek style, though somehow out of kilter with its own Imperial gold-tiled roof. Each visitor had to pass by a statue of Mao seated, then the interior was shadowy until one approached the death chamber. In a brilliantly lit crystal sarcophagus he lay, dressed in a gray tunic, a flag draped across the bier.

The two notables were ushered through in a few minutes. Outside, the crowd was much smaller. The President's adviser indicated to Jarrell that an order of wonton, for himself and Ms. Jones-Russell, should be brought to the stone bench under the small arch to the left of the building; and that he and Ms. Jones-Russell would spend a half hour more there before returning to the American Embassy for the farewell luncheon which he was to host for the Politburo of the PRC.

"Much lighter than Lenin's," she said, "they're so different—the Russians are tragic and the Chinese are . . . ah, thank you, Mr. Jarrell. (Can I give *you* a bite? . . . I don't think that young man understands me, do you?")

"Yes," he nodded, "that's what Mr. Hu has made me understand, over the years, how different the Russians and the Chinese are from each other."

"And the Americans," she said, "except that we can all interbreed, unlike in the old Stone Age when there were actually two races of *sapiens.*"

"Oh, shut up and eat," he said.

The wonton tasted as delicious as it smelled. "What else is there?" she said, "I was ravenous . . . Mao's crypt is almost cheerful compared to Lenin's. Umm, this is fantastic . . . Ah, Wolf, what is the use of this cult of the dead? People want to breathe and eat and love—"

She had finally touched some embattled zone inside him. "This *is* the Forbidden City. Here the imperial secrets were born and died behind the high red walls. The sages preached that they alone knew the secrets of life and their bodyguards cut off the heads of any who doubted it. Dynasty after dynasty . . . and now the made-up man who looks like a wax dummy lies in perpetual state. The point is that Washington and London, Moscow, they're all forbidden cities like this, in the sense of secrecy and power. My field is the management of conflicts, *not* the acting out of the role of the saint, martyr or madman. I, personally, have no power. It's because of the fact that I represent the United States that I have influence. The moment that I say or do anything contrary to the basic interests of power in America, I am instantly yesterday's hero. Even Mao knew it. He told André Malraux, before he died, 'I am alone with the people—waiting.' "

"No, Wolf, don't tell me that you're only following orders. Don't you believe freedom is power? The *old* idea of power is that wax dummy under the glass in there?"

On the periphery Jarrell was whispering into his walkie-talkie.

The sun was high, making a crescent of white around the arch's shadow in which they sat. Wolf's eyes were bright as he looked at her hair, then down to her open coat and in at the outline of her breasts, then up again to her face.

"B. J., we're talking at cross-purposes. I'm saying that my power is only managerial. You're talking about—"

"T.A.G.—the allegedly great. The people you work for are not great, authentically, in their own right, only in inverse ratio to public passivity."

"Well, I don't believe in 'Men of Destiny' any more than I do the ignoramuses in the White House or the crackpots at CIA and the NSC. I don't *believe* in Napoleon or Moses or Mao: so far as

I'm concerned they're *all* the product of . . . mass mythomania, to put it your way. To me they're all T.A.G., Betsy. The *allegedly* great."

"You're merely a manager . . . What do you think I want, for you to be a god in a machine come to save the human race?"

"Do you?"

"Wolf, I think I want to *live* with you. We're all afraid to die. Everyone, even crisis managers know that, so why can't you just say it—publicly?"

"B. J., you talk like we were at the end of history. My brief is more humble: I am negotiating with two nations about to go to war with each other so that if worst comes to worst then we, the West —or some of us, anyway—can escape . . . to carry on . . . Look, Jarrell is signaling to us that security is ready to have us move back to the Embassy—"

"Screw Mr. Jarrell—what do you mean 'the end of history?' What do you think a war between Russia and China will lead to? How dare you patronize me! It's you who's the idealogue. You actually *believe* that a nuclear exchange between China and Russia won't spill into Europe and then the rest? If you don't believe that, why are the wires carrying a story that the President will address the nation after your return and that a source suggests that he may announce an emergency Civil Defense mobilization?"

"That's on the wires?"

"It is."

"Betsy, I didn't mean to insult your intelligence, how could I since you are, in many ways, wiser than I am. But you have to understand that if the U. S. appeals to the U. N. then we would lose the entire thrust of secret diplomacy—"

"Exactly, Wolf. With all due apologies to Metternich and Bismarck and Castlereagh and Pitt—and their generic descendants down through Kissinger and Brzezinski to yourself—none of that has ever worked beyond the time it took the printer's ink of the headlines to dry. The twentieth century is a slaughterhouse. The only thing the bright, best 'action intellectuals' and longheaded strategic thinkers have done is to rationalize death. Because in their little hearts they must not believe that *they* will go with the rest of us. Dreaming that they get on a jet, or hide in an underground city and live on among the corpses; but their children will burn like ours, or like mine if I can have one. They're like the Jews in Germany—I mean the German Jews thought that because they were *Germans* they would be exempt. You know that."

"Some, yes. I was not exempt. My father was murdered at Buchenwald, my mother's life was destroyed by what had happened to Germany. I was a part of the uprising at Buchenwald. I know that you have to fight."

"But Wolf, when you say 'fight' or 'Munich' or, like the Israelis, 'Never again!' you're singing the anthem of another crisis, from another time. Is it necessary to be a permanent adolescent? Saigon wasn't Munich, nor is Afghanistan or Iran or the Thai border. Neither the Soviets nor the Chinese are Nazis, so why are you thinking in World War II terms? Why can't you people understand that *a nuclear holocaust is unthinkable!*"

"Don't try to tyrannize me, Dr. Russell, and do not even flirt with the idea of playing on what you seem to think is my survival guilt. I'm afraid I believe that wars and revolutions arise out of the drives of the human race. We seem to be fighting animals.

"Rubbish . . . crackpot anthropology—"

"I'm the son of a first-rate anthropologist. We stand, barely, somewhere between apes and angels, we're the most sophisticated predator the world has ever known—"

"God, Wolf, if you're going to jabber on about 'territorial imperatives,' what's the use in going on—"

"Wait a minute, for the first time in my life someone has made me *think* about bringing a child into this nightmare. That's reason enough to go on, isn't it? . . . You'd be a superb mother." He covered his mouth, though Jarrell and the SS were huddled over a radio and not looking at them. "Maybe I could be the father ... No, don't move, they're watching us again and there's still press over there."

She closed her eyes and waited for her breathing to return to normal. She fumbled in her shoulder sack to find a cigarette to break. There was a light film of perspiration on her forehead. While her eyes were shut he flashed a five-minute signal with his hand to Jarrell, who promptly turned back to his walkie-talkie. The dim wails of the shadowboxers had a Greek, an immemorial arc and fall.

He leaned toward her. "B.J., I'm caught between these Nation-States. It's wearing me down I admit. It's a world of victory on victory—as in *1984*—triumph after triumph: an endless pressing on the nerve of power . . ." His face was pulled back and taut. She turned to him, her blue eyes almost gray in the shadow.

"You think I'm a compulsive womanizer. That's in the columns. Did you know that I haven't 'been' with anyone for over a year. Until you."

Dark shadows rippled across them as a cloud crossed the sun's path and turned the color of their skin almost blue. For the moment of shadow their eyes could rest.

He said, "I'm trying to think. That's all I'm doing, trying to think how we—all of us—can get out in front of this vicious circle of—"

She reached up and touched his forehead. Let the SS watch, she thought. He didn't flinch, his eyes just widened a little.

"The forty-eight percent in the latest polls who favor the use of nuclear weapons if the Russians refuse to back down—"

"But, Wolf, if the world is going mad doesn't that make your responsibility all the greater to, well, go *sane?*"

"And how do I do that, Betsy," very softly. "When the numbers go over fifty percent?

"By becoming a 'majority of one,' Wolf. By quitting and going public. Orwell said that there was truth and there was untruth and that if you clung to the truth even against the whole world—that *then* you were not mad."

The clouds were past and the sun's rays lit him from the back. His face was strained in its inward intensity. She thought she could see the pulse in his temple start up.

"And what about the vanity of thinking that you alone can somehow tell truth to power? Orwell came back from Spain cursing the Communists and Fascists equally. At the end he pictured people as worn out dray horses being ruled by a gang of pigs—"

"He was dying in 1949—"

"As we may be in 1984—"

"It's our job to live, to *save* life if not to produce it. No, let me go on. Go to your state luncheon, I'm going to the airport. No, I said I'm going."

She stood over him, half in shadow, part of her in the sunlight. "I knew that it would take a crisis for me to get over my great man complex. I owe you that."

"I repeat, I'm merely the representative of the United States of America." He smiled up at her, at least with his lips. His eyes looked hollow now.

"You know what Chairman Mao said, 'Though death befalls all men alike, it may be heavier than Mount Tai or lighter than a feather—' "

"Will you stop quoting great men! Especially *dead* great men. If you love me then love *me*. You've gone through your career looking for giants and heroes—searching for some god like B.R. that you could love in effigy, and it can't be done. I'm just who I am— that's all. My *father* was a hero. I'm just his son."

"Wolf, you Jews have a very wise saying that when you die, God will not ask you why you were not Moses or your father or any other hero—God will simply ask you why you were not *yourself.* Why you were not Wolf Manheim . . . Wolf," she said as she turned,

"I'll interview you, I'll leak your party line for you, and I'll fuck you. But don't talk about love to me without survival. That's necrophilia, that's the love-death of the camps . . . I'm getting out of here. I'll see you in Washington."

As she strode away from him, past the knot of bodyguards, she flung the dark glasses at Jarrell without pausing. "Here, Mr. Jarrell, use these to hide the eyes in the back of your head."

13

BUCHENWALD—JULY, 1944

The man, Kantsler, kept making the awful sounds. When the boy could not stand any more he ran into the room just as the doctor, his father, finished killing Kantsler with his bare hands.

The tall, lifeless body slid down and sprawled on the carbolic clean floor of the Staff Room. Scores of others must have heard the screams, yet no one had appeared except the boy. A vein in his father's forehead was pumping as he stared at the boy and caught his breath. Outside the heavily shaded window was hot July day, but inside it was still, for the moment, and shadowy cool. "Shut the door," the doctor said, and sat down heavily, his powerful hands on his knees.

"This is Kantsler, our man in the 'Canada' . . . Wolfie, do me a favor, sit down. Please. I have to talk to you. You know about Canada?"

The boy knew all about the Canada. Buchenwald, like every other camp, was a machine for robbing and stripping each new arrival, storing the booty and treasure, then shipping it back to the Reich. This system involved thousands of inmates and gigantic

157

warehouses; warehouses overflowing with clothing and tins of food, drugs, liqueurs and sweets—this the inmates called "Canada." The boy knew Canada because for more than three months one of his jobs had been to run drugs and medicines from Warehouse 19 back to the hospital. And he had seen the Canada Kapo, Kantsler, any number of times making the rounds, barking orders. Now he was dead, sprawled on the floor like the broken clown in the ballet, *The Shoemaker of Munich,* that his mother had taken him to see and at which he had cried and cried.

The goods from the Canada had come under the control of the camp underground after ferocious fights with the original criminal kapos, the Greens, and now provided the barter for the manipulation of the SS. Meats, liqueurs, clothing, jewelry were lavished on key SS by the underground. The boy knew that it went on. "But wasn't Mr. Kantsler a leader in the underground?"

"Let me tell you about Mr. Kantsler," the doctor said. "Relax yourself for a few minutes. They're all asleep after the noon food, until it cools off; the workers won't be back for hours yet . . . Mr. Kantsler was a former accountant from Breslau—that is why we put him at the head of our bank. Mr. Kantsler was clever with figures, too clever as it turned out. We discovered that he was holding back on drugs and running a combination with SS enlisted men who in turn were selling on the Weimar black market. Here, as you know, the security of the group comes first, and I'm afraid that Mr. Kantsler, when he got into trouble—as he must when thieves fall out—would be denounced by the SS. The SS would then have *their* man ready to go in as head of Canada, and their man would, in his turn, denounce the underground. You see, Wolfie, why Mr. Kantsler had to be done away with, before he hung himself, and the rest of us with him?" The doctor looked over the boy's head into the gloom for a moment then heaved himself up and poured hot coffee for the two of them from the two-burner staff stove, and sat down again. The boy was watching a beam of sunshine as it spread along the base of the shade and spilled over onto the sill. The body on the floor was still in shadow.

"Wolfie, you ask why . . . It's time to tell you certain things that you have to know. You have to be a big boy now, a man, *verstehst du?* Millions in gold and jewels flow through Canada. That money is for the purchase of guns and bombs—we are going to destroy this place down to the last stick. *That* you didn't know, did you? The bank notes we use for toilet paper, but the gold . . . listen, Wolfie, Germany is *kaput;* another year and it will be over. But the question is whether they will first destroy this camp and the others like them down to the last man, under the cover of the Allied bombing attacks—which must eventually come. Most of the SS are ruined as men, and thanks to the Canada we can turn most of them into drunkards who, we hope, will run away at the end. But there are enough animals who, under orders, would blow up the camp to bury their crimes. That is why we are preparing for an inmate uprising, a struggle to be timed with the Allied advance, when it comes. We must, at least, be able to take over the machine-gun tower and the blockhouses. That is why Kantsler and others like him—informers, criminals—must be killed. That is why we must kill people in the hospital as well as trying to save and hide others. We are not just trying to save our own skins. We have limited power and we must use it to pick and choose, against the day of the uprising."

The boy tried not to look at the dead man. He hung on the doctor's story.

"The Allied bombing has already badly hurt the factories around Dachau, Sachsenhausen, Auschwitz, as well as here by Weimar. It is only a matter of time. The first survivors of Lublin and the eastern camps will be pouring in here by August first—we know this from our intelligence system. These prisoners will be living corpses, driven by forced march across Europe ahead of the Russian advance. They will be hard to control, they've tasted blood—they slaughtered SS men at Lublin before reinforcements overwhelmed them. Our well-ordered operation here will be chaos overnight. We will have nationality grouping. Secrecy is basic to our plan. No one outside of the underground must know where our stores of carbines and pistols and grenades are hidden. No, even you, my son, must not know. No one can stand SS torture . . . And when these skeletons from the East start to pour in here, the SS are going to get crazy, there will be 'incidents'—anything could happen—and we must not permit provocation to preempt our chances . . . What I'm telling you, Wolfie, is that what is coming will make the time since you arrived here—even this—look like a family holiday. Do you think you will be able to stand it?"

Strauss stuck his head in at that moment to report to the doctor. Headquarters had sent word that Major Ding-Schuyler would be making rounds after 3:00 P.M. Without a word Strauss reached down and grabbed the corpse's collar, then lugged the body out and kicked the door shut behind him. Where the dead man had sprawled, a single white button was left on the floor to catch the light. The boy stared down at the pink tips of his bitten fingernails.

"Dr. Ding-Schuyler is a decent man . . . Yes, I know, he's very weak, but he will help us when the time comes, if he lasts . . ." The boy watched the broad back as the doctor poured himself more hot coffee. The streak of sunlight was trembling around the wooden slat at the shade's end. "Without Ding-Schuyler there would be no underground radio, we would not know how close the front was . . . *ach,* what all this means day to day for you, son, is that you will see—as you saw today—terrible things . . . lying, cheating, killing, every kind of trick. All this, when *we* do it, we call resistance, preparation for the revolt. We *do* all this yet we must not become taken over by what we do. Can you understand me? Unfortunately, son, the best do not survive here . . . little Father Thyle did not last. That is why I am telling you that you must learn to lie and cheat and *kill*—to survive . . . You may ask me why, why should anyone want or need to survive this way? It's a fair question. You're right, some of our people have become more animal than the SS. There is no contradiction for them between what they *do* and who they *are*—they *are* whips, boots, clubs . . . whereas we others only *imitate,* pretend to be like the SS so that they will leave us alone to run this place, which is all we have. Survival here is an achievement, not an individual accident. Always remember that, Wolfie . . . It is our excuse . . ."

Strauss and the orderly Peiper walked in to get mugs of coffee and left without a word. Everyone knew that after August first would come the beginning of the end. The camp, meanwhile, seemed to be hanging in some timeless dream of July. The smoke-stacks of Weimar puffed in the distance. The good citizens of the town who had profited enormously from the combined suffering of the camp went about their daily routine unaware of the revenge being plotted on them inside a thousand shaved skulls.

In the heat of the day the camp streets were deserted. The slave battalions were miles away being murdered in the rock quarries or ground up in the wheels of the Krupp plants. Frau Koch's horses stamped in their shadowy stables while she and Dr. Ding-Schuyler dallied in her darkened bedroom. Her husband, the Camp Commandant, worked away at the marigolds in his formal garden. In the hot sun the shiny worms turned in the earth under his manicured hand.

Now the explanations were over and there was more urgency in the doctor's voice. "Starting tomorrow you will replace our orderly to the women's camp. You will deliver the medicine—nothing more —until August. By August we will have made contact with the Allies. You will be told what to do, but don't get friendly with *anyone.* When a guard makes an inmate pregnant we have to kill the infant in order to let the mother live. Himmler's orders leave no question there—so we have to pass them off as stillborn. There is no pity here, Wolfie. The pure in heart like Father Thyle suffer the least damage to their souls, if you call it that, and they bless us, whose hands are red. We are going to survive in order to testify, to bear witness—for no other reason. Wolfie, at Treblinka they were burning fifteen thousand a day, women and children too. Their *Sonderkommando,* the prisoners who operated the death factory, organized a revolt one year ago, and they burned it down and a handful escaped—and their story will be told, and ours will be told.

"At Treblinka, the survivors told us, the moment that one of the group ate something without sharing, it was the beginning of the end for him . . . though Treblinka no longer exists, we now understand this: At Treblinka they died in their thousands, but they took their executioners down with them."

Somewhere in the camp a whistle blew. Soon roll call and evening slops, soon the slave columns would be returning in the evening; already from miles away the balmy breeze had begun to blow the poison of their combined stench ahead into the nostrils of the camp. The incredible stench, on the breeze, of blood and wasted bodies crept through the hospital; even the carbolic acid could not cut it. The boy reached the wastebasket, getting sick on the lumps of sausage and pickles that his father had insisted he eat.

"That's right," the doctor said behind him, "you're smelling the whirlwind. The whole world has got to be made to smell it. We must make *them* vomit up their insides, too, and fall to *their* knees crying, crying as you are now. Remember Father Thyle—'the sickness unto death' and how he said Jesus Christ was coming? Well, we know that a wind is rising, you can smell it from far off, nothing can escape its path, no one will be spared."

The big bear of a man had been shouting in hoarse bursts, then the boy's eardrums were ringing from his own screaming, inside his head. "TO EACH HIS OWN!" The smell was pulling his viscera up into his throat, his whole body heaving.

"Peyser," the doctor shouted, "come! *He's having a seizure.*"

14

WASHINGTON, D.C.—JANUARY 25, 1984
(WEDNESDAY)

BETSY JONES-RUSSELL: The President is going to the U.N.? When will this be announced?

W.M.: I announce it—to you, Ms. Russell.

B.J-R.: Thank you, sir . . . Now, may I ask you, Dr. Manheim, whether the administration has been sobered by the worldwide reaction? In Paris, Rome, Berlin, London, Amsterdam there are, at this moment, major demonstrations—the largest, reportedly, since World War II.

W.M.: I'm sorry, I thought I just said that the President—

B.J-R.: Yes, but can you be believed?—I mean *will* you be believed? This morning's Washington *Post* states that U.S. Navy ships are moving out of Guantánamo, in blockade formation, against both Cuba and Jamaica. This is drastic, Mr. Secretary, if it's true.

W.M.: American forces have been on the alert since the Soviet ultimatum to the People's Republic of China on January third . . . May

163

I ask why you are calling me Mr. Secretary?

B.J-R.: Because Washington is full of the news that the President, in his speech, will announce that Mr. Higgins has stepped down and that you will assume the role of National Security Adviser and Secretary of State, as Henry Kissinger once did. I know that you can't comment on any of this so if I may pursue another line . . . Mr. Hilary Kn'Eno of Uganda has delivered a speech in New York, before the U.N., stating, in part, "The three superpowers do not challenge each other in Europe where the armies of the Warsaw Pact and NATO stare down the barrels of each other's guns . . ." and he goes on to accuse the big nuclear powers of using the bushes of Africa, the deserts of the Middle East, the jungles of Southeast Asia and the mountains of Pakistan-Iran-Afghanistan as the "killing ground." His denunciation of the USSR and, equally, the U.S. and China—whom he linked—received an ovation, and there are reports of thousands of people gathering in front of the U.N. complex—

W.M.: I do not yet have a copy of Mr. Kn'Eno's remarks. I am aware of some turmoil in New York. (Sidney, get me Kn'Eno.—oh, thank you.) Ms. Russell, I hope you will demand of Mr. Arbatov, the Soviet representative, whether or not *they* will also renounce any aggressive use of nuclear devices.

B.J-R.: Mr. Secretary, *you* will be meeting with Mr. Arbatov this week, will *you* urge him to work toward a joint statement condemning the Chinese ultimatum?

W.M.: Well, I think the Soviets' responsibility for their situation has to also be assessed. It is, after all, the Soviet support for the insurgency right across the Horn of Africa that is provoking the South Africans, with *their* nuclear capacity, in the most dangerous manner. It is the Soviets behind the Vietnamese face-off with China on *two* borders, the Soviets that have a brigade of amphibious troops stationed in the island of Cuba . . . and I hope you will inquire of Mr. Arbatov concerning the reports over the weekend of mass arrests in Lithuania and the Ukraine, including the doctors and scientists in the prestigious "Helsinki Group". (Sidney, get him

and him over here for a lunch meeting—twelve noon sharp.) Please
go on, Ms. Russell.

B.J-R.: Does the United States intend at the United Nations to renounce or renew its Mutual Assured Destruction or "MAD" policy?

W.M.: You are nothing if not persistent, Ms. Russell. (Andrew, you
can hear for yourself what she's getting. You talk to Jim about
getting a completely new and *secure* phone system between here
and the EOB and the President by this afternoon. I'm *serious* about
this. Please turn off the tape, B.J. Never mind—goddamn it, Andrew, get on it *now!*) . . . I'm sorry Ms. Russell. You understand,
I'm sure. Ah, your question was . . . ?

B.J-R.: Is the United States still MAD?

W.M.: The United States has, through some seven administrations,
been committed to the unfortunately so-called MAD position, as
indeed has the Soviet Union. It is for this reason that the Administration has made the commitment to the MX missile. The alterna-
tive is, of course, the old policy of "massive retaliation" in which
case all major American and Russian cities are held hostage.

B.J-R.: But Dr. Manheim, if the MX knocks out the silos of the
Soviet "second strike" reserve, then doesn't it stand to reason that
if the Russians *did* launch a first strike that it would be *total* and
not limited to silos? Isn't that what *every* reputable international
expert insists?

W.M.: It stands to reason, Ms. Russell, that since both sides have the
firepower to destroy the other many times over that the Soviets will
not contemplate a nuclear war. It would be unthinkable and—

B.J-R.: But for over two weeks the USSR, the U.S. and the PRC have
been threatening *exactly* such an "unthinkable" eventuality.

W.M.: Not the United States.

B.J-R.: How do we *know?*

W.M.: I believe that the diplomatic process *is* working, Ms. Russell.
(Fifteen minutes, Andrew. What? No, onion soup or something.) . . .

B.J.-R.: Thank you for your time today. Can we expect a statement after your meeting this evening with the "wise men"?

W.M.: I beg your pardon?

B.J-R.: It is common knowledge, Dr. Manheim, that a secret meeting will take place somewhere in the Washington area tonight. And it will include such *old* Cold War soldiers as Clark Clifford, John J. McCloy, the Bundy brothers, Dean Rusk and John McCone, not to mention David Packer, James Schlesinger—

W.M.: . . . No comment. (Peter, get me the President.)

B.J-R.: Thank you, Dr. Manheim.

W.M.: Thank you, Dr. Russell.

MANHEIM WAS LEFT OUT OF NEW NUCLEAR WAR STRATEGY PLANS
National Security Chief tells reporters he learned of policy decision by reading news stories

BY

B.J. RUSSELL

WASHINGTON—National Security Adviser Wolfgang Manheim —shades of ex-Secretary-of-State Muskie four years ago?— doesn't understand why he learned about the President's decision to revise American nuclear war strategy only when informed about it by a member of the press.

Speaking with unusual candor to a half dozen reporters on his Air Force plane flying back from China Monday night, Manheim said that a matter with such important foreign policy implications should have been discussed with him as well as with other advisers before the President acted. He said that he is trying to find out what happened and why he was bypassed by Defense Secretary Arnold Bannister and Air Force General Victor Karmer.

(Please turn to page 3)

15

WASHINGTON, D.C.—JANUARY 25, 1984
(WEDNESDAY NIGHT)

She was staring out the window at the beam of the helicopter's landing lights when someone pushed her door buzzer. It's him, she thought, the anger melting, wanted to hold and touch him, to salve the wound of the morning's interview. Thinking, as she walked to the door, We're so difficult, so temperamental that we deserve each other, she opened the door to find Andrew Kott.

She stared down at him and reached back to flick on the foyer light. He brushed past her.

Kott was only thirty-six but she could tell what he would look like as an old man—bandy-legged, pot-bellied, bald. At the moment a heavy raincoat flapped around the contours of his stubby, three-piece-suited body. His sideburns were thick and curly, his pate was shiny, his eyes were red behind the old-fashioned black rims of the glasses. He's been drinking vodka, she thought, that's why you can't smell anything. He moved toward the kitchenette as if the

167

beam of the circling helicopter would come through the window and find him.

"Come in here please." He had the very correct speech of those who learned their English in London.

"Well, Mr. Kott—" she began, but stopped when he gestured her to come close while with his right arm he pointed around the sitting room ceiling, making the universal symbol for electronic surveillance.

It was 7:00 P.M. and she was tired from a long day of interviewing and dictating to London. The big story had been that nothing was happening or would happen, it seemed, until after the President's U.N. speech and Manheim's meeting with the USSR's Arbatov. Nothing fazed, London was building front-page stories out of quotes pulled from her interviews with Wolf, and she was having to battle to hold on to the context, and now here was Mr. Kott looking a bit crazy and hiding in her kitchen.

Kott turned on the faucets, hard. She could see his eyes and knew that, whatever amount of vodka he may have consumed, he was not drunk. The water rattled off the aluminum sink. She leaned back against the counter, across the narrow kitchen aisle, and he came and stood at her ear. He waited a moment for his own breathing to settle and the helicopter to complete its arc.

"I am going to have to leave here in about two minutes," he said softly in his formal accent, under the spatter of the running water. "I'm going to leave you the working papers for the meeting that begins at eight with the President's advisers. This is a blueprint; there will not be any substantial changes. Dr. Manheim's task will then be to fly to California with it and sell it to the military and CIA. It is the least belligerent plan we could hope to devise. It gives the Soviets at least a face-saving way out. Dr. Manheim will take this to Arbatov and it will sound like an ultimatum but it is not— or maybe it is, but it is the best we can do. Arbatov must believe that." He turned aside to open his attaché case and take out a thick blue sealed folder. "It will be inside here."

So Wolf did love her; no, that was a stupidly selfish way to understand the man's dilemma. He had sent his aide to her, the interviews must be only part of it, he needed her help. She looked at the young man, who was only slightly older than she but seemed a cynical cherub by comparison, and nodded as if she understood completely. He held her by the arm as he confided to her ear.

"So the advisers will tinker with it, but then tomorrow it goes to Califor—"

"You don't mean *tomorrow?*" she whispered.

"Yes. He won't have time to see you. The President is going to postpone his Friday morning speech to the U.N. until *after* the Manheim-Arbatov meeting—"

"But that will—"

"It will get the Soviets' attention, that's what it will do. So, I will leave it with you. I am putting myself in your hands, I could go to prison for this. I am hoping that as an international figure you will find a way to talk to Mr. Arbatov, whom I believe you have interviewed previously, and present our case."

The water sputtered; she stared at him. It was not necessary— or possible—to say anything now. "I have to go," the red-eyed young man said, "the advisers will already be coming in . . . If anything goes wrong, please remember that *I* brought you the documents—" he paused—"for my own reasons. Good-bye." He walked toward the foyer with a sort of stubby dignity, then cracked the door, and apparently finding no lurking Secret Service, stepped quickly out.

His own reason, she remembered, would be the wife from Texas, Molly, and the afflicted child . . . What was its name? She could visualize the smooth leather photo wallet that Kott had held out to her on the plane with shaky fingers. Curious, his hands had not seemed to tremble tonight when he passed the documents, unless it had been too dark to see. Did this little man actually have more courage and conscience than anyone else? . . . Halina, that was the child's name. At least he *had* a child, something to make him pause, something to relieve a little of the self-centeredness of the National Security Council and its "40 Committee," its "Room 303," its "10/2," its countless secret acronyms and mnemonic devices. And *Wolf* obviously relied on him . . . .

She could still see the intensity burning in Andy Kott's little eyes, telling her something more. Yes—it would not be enough to simply deliver the NSC document to the Soviet Ambassador. It was expected that she bring back some *response* from Arbatov. Extraordinary. No longer just the provocative reporter . . . now an actor in the drama . . .

She walked slowly back to the kitchenette to turn off the water and pick up the envelope with the working paper or whatever it was called, but she was already thinking about calling Soviet Special Ambassador Arbatov, who had been her lover at a critical moment in her life in 1970.

She decided that she would take a bath before she put the call in. The Watergate bathtubs were oversized and deep . . . She lay back to soak and gather not strength but stamina for the night that lay ahead. As the heat began to unlock the tension, she slid further down, eyes closed, thinking of Georgi Arbatov the first time she had met him, at a memorial service for B.R. in London when she was only twenty years old . . . .

The funeral itself had been private. Some two dozen family and intimates had accompanied Lord Russell's plain oak coffin from Plas Penrhyn to the Colwyn Bay crematorium. From there she had returned to London to help with the reorganization of the Foundation offices. Two weeks later, on February 20, an international memorial ceremony had been held at the Phillips Hall. The speaker from the Soviet Union was Georgi Arkadyevich Arbatov, at that time chief of the Soviet Institute of World Economy and International Relations, and a recognized expert on Anglo-American institutions. His remarks were simply phrased yet subtle in their description of the long and problematical relationship between the British lord and the Soviet Union. The Russian's intense eyes met hers as he concluded his encomium.

Afterward, when she approached, he had asked if she would stay a moment to join him in a glass of champagne. An hour later they were the only ones left in the old hall that had been a Russell favorite since the war resistance days of 1916. Generations of rhetoric had resounded in this wooden auditorium, built at the end of the eighteenth century and soon to be razed. Yet so cunning were the acoustics that their voices carried around the mezzanine.

"We toasted him on his last birthday with some of this same wine," she said.

"Were you related to him?" he asked. His apology over the state of his English was quite unnecessary, she assured him; not only were syntax and grammer perfect, but his modest funeral oration had struck just the right note.

She knew from the London *Times* only that he was forty-seven years old, a native of Kherson, and a hero in the Great Patriotic War, as the Russians referred to World War II. She studied him as he talked, flattered that he had read some of her first profiles in the *Times.* As with most men he was perhaps a bit shorter than she, yet his posture and an expressive, well-toned body compelled an impression of controlled power and subtle intelligence. His face was oval with an almost delicate snub to the nose; well-formed ears and a high forehead completed the dignified if somewhat typical exterior. It was the eyes, she decided, soft yet full of energy, that set him apart. His dark suit was unexpectedly well cut and she found herself listening and enjoying the experience, especially the subtle, sensuous gestures that he used to amplify his comments about Lord Russell and his place in the history of science and philosophy.

Late supper at the Soviet Embassy. As they sat down alone to caviar and more champagne, the idea of interviewing Georgi (as he

insisted on being called) came to her. "Interview me? But of course
—on condition that we stretch the process out at least as long as
the Geneva talks." The mention of Geneva led her to ventilate her
obsession with the Vietnam War, and his response, which included
a reminiscence of Ho Chi Minh, was so evocative that she perceived
what she had sensed was a link, somehow, between G.A. Arbatov
and Bertrand Russell.

Some combination of this feeling of trust and the champagne led
her to take the unusual step of telling him about her relationship
to Lord Russell, and about his last days. When he listened it was
with his entire concentration, his eyes, almost Oriental at the cor-
ners, wrapping her in their gaze.

". . . After '68 he couldn't speak in public without notes. If you
knew B.R.—we only referred to him that way—in the old days, it
was terrible to see the quick stride and ramrod carriage begin to
change to a slow shuffle . . . Sometimes his face would go slack, you
know, and this gave a very false impression of senility because the
mind burning inside was still precise and lucid. But he was happier,
you know, perhaps than he had ever been in his entire life. His
fourth wife was a godsend . . . and his rage for life, real life, was
as strong as ever. Oh, dear, but it does feel good to let down a bit
and talk too much . . . ah, you are kind . . . I'll test *you* now. His
last birthday toast was to 'the silent ones—whether in Eastern
Europe or behind the walls of Pentonville or Brixton.' There! What
do you say to that?"

The Russian's laugh was a throaty chuckle. His lips were full and
she could not seem to keep herself from watching them move as he
spoke, so that she only caught a fragment of what he said. And then
she was reminiscing again, letting him draw her out.

". . . he seemed to get a bit more tired each day . . . But—this
was so typical—the last week he had received a letter from someone
containing what he thought to be a dishonest proposal and so he
dictated an immediate reply to me. Five minutes later he was

terribly distressed to find that I hadn't yet left to post it. It was as if the house was unclean until the offending missive was disposed of . . . and I didn't grasp the urgency. That last Sunday, February first, he leaned on my shoulder to look over the Ffestiniog Valley one more time . . . then on the Monday he felt rather ill about seven in the evening . . . he was gone within the hour."

As he came around to her side of the massive old table she rose so that he could put his arms around her. His muscular forearm around her waist guided her, as surely as if he had lifted her in his arms, up the curving staircase to the guest bedroom maintained for foreign dignitaries.

The guest quarters were rather simple and old fashioned, especially the canopied bed with the slippery green quilt. On the wall was a single picture, a print of old Saint Petersburg. "Before it became Leningrad," Georgi laughed, "it was the city that Fyodor Dostoevski said was the city that could not be trusted."

They stood side by side, looking at the dull rendering of the expanse of the Nevsky Prospect. "White nights," she murmured, wanting him to take her. "I've heard it said that you are irresistible because you make it a practice to quote Lenin in the East and Dostoevski in the West."

He turned toward her with his head tipped to one side and almost a childish grin; he reached up to stroke her forehead and then put his fingertips in her hair. "You think I'm too clever?" he asked.

"By half," she said.

She was ravishingly beautiful at twenty, to say nothing of the sophistication the life of a London journalist afforded her, yet he sensed that her encounters with men had not been fulfilling, that her overriding passion had, like Russell's, been lavished on the "farthest man" and not on a lover near at hand.

He undressed her slowly. She watched as his square but sensitive hands moved over her body, removing the dress and undergarments as if he were working with flowers. When he returned to the bed, naked, her eyes were closed while her mind, like her flesh below, was both open and dark. *"Devochka,"* he murmured, and *"dousha, lubov,* my girl, my love . . . "

The first complete orgasm of her life came when he gently put his hand on her own and then moved both together down onto the throbbing clitoris. Slowly he started her touching herself. When she could no longer stop, his hand went off to explore the rest of her. Then he guided her other hand up to her breasts and around the flesh of her erect nipples. Then, again, he explored her as her hips began to tremble and jerk independently of the rest of her. She opened her eyes to meet his gaze as he slowly mounted her; pressing her hands to continue touching herself as his thick yet strangely graceful body began its slow thrust and recover.

It began to snow that night and in her memory it never stopped. Every day for two weeks they met for their "interview." She, who had heretofore covered her striking beauty with clothes out of the 1950s, appeared suddenly in the snowbound streets of the "bandaged town" in garments still simple but now wonderfully cut, showing off her figure as the tweed skirts grazed her kneecaps, hitting just above her calves. The blouses and sweaters, too, no longer came to just below her chin, but were sometimes left unclasped to yield a glimpse of her full breasts, other times hugging the body to show the gentle inward slope toward her waist. For the first time, too, splashes of color appeared—a casually tied floral scarf setting off her neck, a bright cotton bandana catching her hair. Overall, this "new look" resembled nothing so much as a free, yet artfully arranged bouquet of flowers, and inside, her body seemed a resonating chamber in which, over and over again, his words— *"Moya doragya,* my darling" resounded.

They talked and they made love. It was odd—and wonderful— that under his hands she came to know herself. She who could not follow her mother's road, who did not know who among men was her father, was in a way reborn in the muscular arms and against the matted chest of the stranger from Moscow.

Sitting until all hours in front of the bedroom fireplace watching his red lips, lips that had that hour left the skin of her whole body stippled as if by a receding wave of blushes, watching him as he told her "fairy stories about Father Stalin and the rebellious sons" . . . confessing to her what it had cost to hide not only his revulsion but his talents after demobilization in 1944, until the tyrant's death in the 1950s. "I drank too much, and married—too much." Telling about his wife, whom he "respected," and his two children, whom he loved. He was, she feared, going out of his way to spread all his limitations out in front of her to apply a brake to the passions he had released.

Near the end he had stopped her protestation, holding her in his arms on the rug in front of the fire, brushing his lips against her hair. "At another time. I wish it too. My wild *devochka,* . . . there are some things we cannot change. History is one of them."

"Georgi, I can't believe that people, you and I, are just straws in the winds of history—"

"No, no. We are *free* . . . within history. But not outside of it. We are not God, or gods—except maybe you, my darling—I am a Marxist and you are a Russell and we both know that we are not God . . . I must leave for home on Wednesday—that gives us three more times together, and you will finally have to finish your interview. I will leave, and I will not write to you, and you will go on living and becoming an important writer and from time to time we will hear something said or read each other's name in the press . . . you see, I'm crying too, like any good Russian." Then he cupped her chin and looked deep into her eyes—"*Dousha,* people who belong together need not be tied together."

The interview of Georgi Arkadyevich Arbatov in the Sunday *Times* by Betsy Jones-Russell was reprinted all over the world. The questions were evocative rather than provocative and the answers, many thought, were the real beginning of Arbatov's reputation in the West as the most human and so hopeful of the younger future leaders in the Kremlin. Tough-minded and clearly one day to be a power in the Politburo, Arbatov phrased his answers so that they would be marked by the public—and remembered by Western intelligence establishments. In fact, the interview was later pointed to as a signal to the Nixon administration that a strategic arms limitation treaty was possible.

The SALT talks had long since collapsed, but Georgi Arbatov had risen high in the Politburo and now represented the Kremlin "doves." It was said that the generals dared not move against him, so great had been his popular base of support ever since the moderates had coalesced around him at the time of the Czechoslovakian debacle. Those against the invasion and its astronomic political cost had included Arbatov, Suslov and the internationalist elite, as well as the officers of the Strategic Rocket Force who knew better than to be threatened by bloc reform. Ranged against the Arbatov realists were representatives of the western regions of the USSR, who felt exposed to the contagion of contiguous reform, the propaganda veterans, and important elements of the KGB and the military. But as in the U.S., the hawks had not yet prevailed, Georgi said.

"You mean that they know a hawk from a handsaw?" she had said, and he shut her up with his lovemaking. That night he had said good-bye to her and left for Moscow . . . .

She knew too well the brief moment on the world stage allowed to the men she wrote about. Her lover of a decade ago had managed to walk the rope stretched across the abyss. There he was now, to meet the other rope dancer, her new love. And she saw herself teetering between the two men . . . Yes, Georgi Arkadyevitch had survived. And as for myself, she thought, I have managed to *love* both sides.

The bath water had lost its heat. She opened her eyes and got out of the tub to telephone the Soviet Embassy.

They sat across a wide table again; alone, again, as the night in London in 1970 when his black eyes had first begun to look into her soul. They were in the massive Washington, D.C., Soviet Embassy building high on the hill that overlooked both the Capitol and the somehow vulnerable eighteenth-century architectural grace of the White House.

She said that he had changed very little, a little more bearlike, deeper around the eyes, gray shot through the neat sideburns, but at sixty-two still enormously virile and magnetic. She started to make a joke about the mausoleum style of the oversized formal room and the chillness of the marble and the modish cut of his gray angora turtleneck sweater.

"You look like your pictures," he leaned across, "glamorous like a film star. You're laughing. Ha! I never thought of defecting but if I did it would have been because of you. Then you were not so sophisticated as now, you were not famous, you were not, ah, experienced and I—"

"Georgi, you bear. I loved you. You *let* me love you . . . you helped me become what I could be, and I will always love you for that. B.R. helped me become a person and you let me become a woman . . . and it's snowing again, too."

She knew that he wanted her, knew that she had to keep her hand on the leather folder in front of her, between them, that personal needs were subsumed for the moment in the larger considerations. Besides, Georgi was her past, the end of her girlhood, while Wolf was, or might be, her future. She now realized that she could never fully love a man again unless there was the possibility of a child, that would not be fair to Georgi. She watched his lips move, as she had before, and pulled her gray cashmere blazer tight against the chill.

"You have been interviewing Manheim—the entire diplomatic world now waits for each day's London *Times, my devochka.* Why has the President canceled his speech to the General Assembly?

What are they playing at? Excuse my excitement. Shall I ring for tea? No. All right. I will let you talk, forgive me but I am concerned, you know . . . and excited."

"Of course. Georgi, I know nothing beyond what you read in my *Times* stories except that Wolf Manheim is as worried as you are. That's why I'm here—I believe—because, in any case, an aide of Wolf's has given me the working paper for tonight's White House meeting of the Cold War *sachems* who, I'm informed, will determine what Manheim lays before you at the week's end after the Joint Chiefs and the CIA unload their—"

"Betsy, wait! You actually have the U.S. proposal *here!*"

"Yes."

"What does it *say?*"

"Georgi, I don't know. I am completely serious. I don't want to know, I want *you* to know. No matter what it says, I can't put it in the *Times,* and I'm damned well not a spy, you know. What I am trying to do, what as I understand it Wolf wants me to do, is to convince you—no matter how belligerent the U.S. position may sound—that there are people like Wolf at the decision-making level who are sane and who do not want to push the button . . . why are you smiling?"

"You refer to the National Security Adviser as 'Wolf.' Why are *you* smiling? No matter, if he passes your test then my opinion of him will have to undergo certain revisions.

"Why? What is your opinion? Seriously, I'm very interested."

"In a minute. Shouldn't we first find out what the Americans have in mind?"

He took the folder between his blunt hands, tore the embossed seal and shook out the purloined carbon copy of the working paper. She watched his face tense and contract as he read the blocks of single space type whose outline she could see through the thin manifold paper.

"You haven't read this?" She shook her head and leaned forward to rest her chin on her hands, as if she were praying.

"*Lubov,* love, this is what the *doves* are going to try to sell the hawks? Your Dr. Manheim is going to march in here to demand, at a *minimum,* the following: One, the removal of all Soviet personnel and facilities from Cuba; two, an agreement to begin negotiations to neutralize the entire Horn of Africa; three, a commitment from the Soviet Union to withdraw all support from the Front Line states in their confrontation with the Union of South Africa; and, finally, a stand-down in southeast Asia leaving Vietnam to negotiate an all-Asian peace treaty—in other words a Chinese-dictated . . . And all this is supposed to be the product of the soft-liners in the National Security Council?" He let the page float down and slide a few inches across the Queen Anne table.

"Georgi, what does the U.S. offer in return?"

He slapped the paper in her direction—"*Nechego.* I assume that Manheim will make vague promises to help 'restrain' the PRC, but there is nothing here in the working paper. I can tell you now that this is totally unacceptable to the Soviet Union. Based on this it is apparent that there have been no comparable demands placed on the PRC. You were there."

"I haven't the faintest idea of what took place in the Hu-Manheim meetings—"

"Betsy, you are a trained observer. These demands imply that it is only the USSR that must give way. On our borders."

"Georgi, southern Africa is not a Soviet border in the—"

"But the Horn of Africa is. And Cuba and Vietnam and, to a lesser degree, the Front Line states are our only allies in their respective continents. Don't you understand, Betsy, this is a U.S.-PRC ultimatum to the Soviet."

He stood, leaning on his fists. "The Soviet people demand," he had told her years before as they talked intimately in front of the fire, "peace and secure borders. And those borders—in the Russian *psychology*—go as far as the Rhine." There was no need for him to tell her any of it again now.

He sat down slowly. Once he had consoled her; now she had to resist the impulse to go to him. Instead she remembered Andrew Kott and the expectant look in his eyes.

"Georgi, what is fair? What is *your* price?"

"You don't wish to become a go-between, but you would like me to entrust to you the Soviet Union's response to this document?"

"Georgi, you have to keep the U.S. talking because there may be much harsher demands added to that list after Wolf takes the heat from the American brass. So, what will you say?"

The deep eyes softened a little. He licked his suddenly dry lips. "It's so ironic, *dousha,* to know that the USSR sees the world in terms of the class struggle while the Chinese 'Third World' concept is based, actually, on color. So that, in the end, after they have used America they will turn on her too. That is what we have sowed— all of us including czarist Russia; yes, and Stalin too made incredible, criminal miscalculations, based on white chauvinism, against the Chinese. I know Mr. Hu for many years, a remarkable man, but he is isolated in his politburo as perhaps I have become—not among my people but in our Politburo—as you tell me Dr. Manheim may be a lone voice of reason with wide popular backing. We shall soon see. Because the Chinese are driven by hate, and *they* play the 'American Card.' "

"Georgi, what, realistically, can you demand in return from the U.S.?"

"All right, you want a list of four points or five points, turn on your tape recorder, and you will take it back and—no? No, I am afraid that your loyalty to peace is at war with your loyalty to Wolf Manheim. I am not saying you are his agent, only his—"

"Lover. That may be, Georgi, and I have been your lover, but that is not the issue. There is tremendous resistance to war and it is breaking out. All over. If nothing happens within a week I'll leak *both* sides. There could be riots in Moscow if the people learn you will even respond—"

"All right, I am sorry. Put on the tape machine. So—first we want the immediate dismantling of nuclear weapon systems and bases in West Germany; number two, we demand that the U.S. likewise dismantle its new nuclear facilities in the People's Republic of China; number three . . ."

"Yes, all right, so at least I'm certain that you have plenty to demand. You feel better now, too, don't you, love?"

"I wish there were time to build a fire and have a proper talk, but thanks to you I have to try to talk sense to Moscow tonight. Ah, but sit a minute or two. You were not just asking rhetorical questions, and I promised to tell you something about your Wolf too."

She wondered if it was still snowing as hard. "I only mean, Georgi, isn't there *something* you can offer? Is the Soviet Union blameless in this crisis? What? *No* blame?"

"How far back into the past do you want to go?" His voice was deep now, somehow more Slavic, the eyes intense.

She shivered, and finally the expression she had seen in his eyes wavered. "You're cold?"

"That, too," she said.

"Take my jacket."

"No, I'll be all right. You were about to—"

"No," he said and stood up. He did not take his eyes from her as he started to walk clockwise around the conference table. Shivering, almost trembling now, she got up and took the five steps it required to meet him halfway at the head of the long table.

"I'm cold, too," he said, and put his arms around her.

Their eyes were level, each to each, for a moment before she embraced him, her entire body contracting, her head angling to meet his lips. While they held each other, two survivors, the cold and the dread seemed to drain away. "My dear *dousha,*" he spoke into her hair, and massaged her back until he was holding, kneading, her buttocks.

"Georgi Arkadyevich . . ." She was warm now. Under his hands she began to pivot and sway, swinging her pelvis in a slow circular arc, then rotating faster, beginning to grind against his fingers and his groin . . . Between her legs a muscle clenched and she was arching her back for him now as her sudden orgasm began. "I'm coming," she gasped, and he held her as she began to tremble uncontrollably, spent herself against the hardness of his body . . .

She could breathe again, "I couldn't help it." Her eyes were closed and her long throat held back so that he could brush her flesh with his lips and say quietly, "We're only human. The poet wrote that 'the opposite of death is desire,' and our bodies tell us what our minds refuse to come to grips with—that we may be close to death."

"Georgi, I can't go on. And I have to go on. I came here to bring and take back a message, not for a *rendezvous* . . ."

The spell was broken. He threw back his head to give room to his basso laughter . . . "My sweet, you are magnificent. Go sit down. I know what to do. Turn back on your tape recorder. and interview me. That's right, laugh, it is absurd, it is grotesque. Interview me, you know that I cannot make love in the presence of a third party, I am not that bourgeois. Go on, ask me the hardest question in your famous giant-killing repertoire. Attack me, demolish my dialectics, devastate my party line. Do it or I will take you now—here—on top of this table, on the marble floor—"

She watched his mouth as he talked against time. Behind him on the white display wall was the traveling Russian avant-garde display of paintings and graphics. His lips had always been mesmerizing to her, she had to fix her gaze to the cubist crosses of Kazimir Malevich and the surreal gigantism of Shchusev who had designed Lenin's mausoleum. "What went wrong?" she asked herself for the thousandth time, looking at the art.

After the storming of the Winter Palace had come that wildly improbable mating of the revolutionary and the avant-garde. From all over Europe, exiled artists streamed home to the new Soviet Union, and with them came the most adventurous souls from all continents. They believed that they would draw and design and film the new Socialist Man . . . then came Stalin to smash the ceramics and rip up the canvasses and shutter the cameras and close the theaters. It was Stalin who had somehow, she knew, fated it that she and Arbatov could never be united. She tried to focus on *Still Life Relief with Hammer,* then on the Kandinskys. "This is Georgi as he would have been," she grieved, listening to him, "bracing, with ferocious energy like these Rodchenkos and Rozanovas." They had all defected to the West after the purges, contributing to European and American art, theater, design—all except Arbatov, who had stayed behind. B.R. had written that Marxism is fundamentally a religion, and all religions become institutionalized in the end. Arbatov was a living priest, still struggling—the resonance of his voice demanding that she look at him . . .

G.A.: . . . The 1980s are different from the 1950s—a cold war with the USSR flies in the face of common sense and the economic, political and military realities of international politics . . . I conclude now please?

B.J-R.: Just a little more, Georgi—I can use a lot of this and it could help.

G.A.: The deployment of the Pershing missiles in Europe was a move which did not get adequate coverage in the U.S. media. It was an enormous setback. All of a sudden we found ourselves surrounded by very mobile long-range nuclear warheads, each with ten times the destructive capacity of the Hiroshima bomb. In a country which lost 12 percent of its population in World War II, this is a nightmare. The U.S. nuclear arsenal was regeared from Massive Retaliation to Flexible Targeting Options. This doctrine allows for "intermediate nuclear warfare"—a Leningrad-for-New York sort of scale.

B.J-R.: And the American-Chinese strategy? Any connection?

G.A.: The notion of a triangular relationship among the United States, the Soviet Union and China does not imply a symmetry of power—contrary to Dr. Manheim's belief. After the Soviet Union and China clashed in 1969, Chinese concern about the Soviet Union led them to consider making an opening to the U.S. to play off the two powers. Now we have the U.S. trying to, in effect, put missiles on our eastern border as they did in Europe.

B.J-R.: One of several interpretations of the decision taken by NATO in Brussels in 1982, to station Pershing 2 and nuclear cruise missiles in Europe, is that the United States wanted to reassure the Europeans.

G.A.: That's a rather far-fetched interpretation to my mind. If Europeans felt the need to be reassured by deployment of new American missiles in Europe, one may ask why the Dutch and Belgian parliaments both voted against it, and why it should stir up such concern among people in Europe who find it more of a danger than anything else.

B.J-R.: But who is stirred up? It was agreed—

G.A.: Not at all. I told you, two parliaments voted against it. The United States imposed the project on the Dutch and Belgian governments anyway, but it was never agreed.

B.J-R.: Italy accepted—

G.A.: The Italians are perhaps more sensitive than others to political and economic pressures.

B.J-R.: And Britain—

G.A.: Britain has very special links with the United States. The British seem to feel that when the United States does something it's a little bit of Britain that's doing it.

B.J-R.: But in France, there was that Communist Party campaign that started after the decision was taken and—

G.A.: It's all the same to me that the French Communist Party, which is not my party, went at things all wrong, as usual . . . And

I am certain that at the present time a certain number of people have decided that a war in Europe is necessary. The USSR is still nothing, its GNP is only half that of Europe. Europe is the world's leading commercial power, like it or not. Now when you're in crisis, when the rest of the Western economies are in desperate trouble, well, it would suit the American economy for Europe to be cut back—"

B.J-R.: I'm ready to believe that they can be cynical, but to *that* degree?

G.A.: I feel so, though I am certain my notions would sound far-fetched to Western ears. Still, I wish at least they would listen and consider. And to make China America's and the world's savior against us is really to be naive beyond all the teachings of history and understanding of the Chinese psychology.

B.J-R.: My! You know, I think I can use this interview if I stay up all night editing. Would you mind?

G.A.: No, not if it is *almost* all night.

They were somewhat healed now by the exchange. She was, she reminded herself, not here to make love or argue but to make certain her two lovers—Wolf and Georgi—went on at least talking long enough for the war fever perhaps to pass. Still . . .

"Georgi, you have to appreciate the Western perception of such things as the detention of dissidents and the silencing of a poet like Igor Broz. *I* signed a petition against it, everybody in London did. Wait—then there's Cubans all over the map of Africa and they're seen as your proxies, and in Cambodia the Soviet backing of the Vietnamese, the meddling in Ethiopia, and so forth. You know that Manheim in an article in *Encounter* magazine wrote that the Soviet pressure on the peripheral areas of the Eurasian continent, the 'rimland'—could lead to Soviet control of the rimland *and* of Eurasia and thus, he concluded, 'who controls Eurasia controls the world'—wait. In the last few years there *have* been pro-Soviet tilts in outright power in Angola, Ethiopia, Southern Yemen, Afghanistan, Central America—all this is believed to be a plot, as you well know, to 'destabilize' rich plums like Iran, Saudi Arabia, etc. I could go on."

"Poets—we're talking, I thought, about world war. Yes, of course, Russia has always tormented and worshipped her writers. You once wrote that Ireland and Russia were mad. That may be true, my Betsy, but I say we are not mad in the way that the U.S. is mad now. We are an ambivalent people—we used to swaddle our infants like little logs of wood so that when they were released they exploded with energy. That is why we drink too much—because we feel too much. That is why we are barely civilized and act like wild animals sometimes, as Chekov wrote so truly. But we *learn,* if slowly. We have changed our immigration policy. We let Jews go who wanted to go *despite* constant Israeli-South African-U.S. propaganda against us. And didn't we reduce troop strength from the Warsaw Pact? And for thanks the U.S. turns the screws in Thailand and plots with China. Paranoid? An overused word but I admit that we have a mortal fear of encirclement, always have. Dr. Manheim has known for some time that if we are required to remove the Chinese nuclear installations then the United States would have only *minutes* to decide whether or not to exchange New York and Washington for the desert nuclear bases of the PRC—"

"Georgi, the U.S., won't exchange them for London and Paris so how—"

"Exactly! Why did the U.S. rearm Japan! And install missiles in Germany? That meant that the warheads could reach the heart of the USSR in six minutes instead of thirty minutes. They took away twenty-four minutes in nuclear time from us! We do not need any more 'Hero Cities.' "

"But didn't Afghanistan—"

"The great reason that we went to the Afghans was the clear signal that Mr. Brzezinski and his 'action intellectuals' had begun to play their 'China Card' in Afghanistan, Pakistan, Cambodia,

Thailand. And the Soviet Union moved to stop that play because we believe that is the beginning of the end. We moved—*yes!* It is the old story of the self-fulfilling prophecy. The U.S. isolates us from the process in the Middle East. At the same time the 'new' CIA was given a blank check for covert schemes in 1980. We had to expose Brzezinski's machinations and we did—"

"And you got Manheim."

"And we got Manheim, and we supposed that there would be a thaw . . . And he *is* much saner, but the process was too far along. The American liberal base was totally split over Israel, the doves of the '60s had become the hawks of the '80s and Manheim, a survivor of Buchenwald, has been a captive of their 'never again!' alarmism. He is a world-renowned political scientist, how could he fail to point out to the warmongers that it is not just the U.S.A. but the USSR too that has 'lost' China and been literally kicked out of Egypt? Where are the military and naval facilities that we once boasted of along the Adriatic? The bases in the Mediterranean, in Algeria, Ghana, Angola, Guinea, the 'great' base in Somaliland from which to *'command'* the Indian Ocean, of the 'dagger's point' in South Yemen?! All gone. (The Angolans actually use Cuban troops to guard American-owned oil companies.) Do you know that we have no allies outside the bloc—"

"Except Cuba—"

"Except Cuba, which costs us ten million dollars a day in aid, and goes its own way into the bargain—but not one great power—we are alone against Sino-American combination, the aim of which —proved by the paper you brought tonight—the aim of which is Soviet capitulation." He pushed his hands through his hair. "You know," his voice was hoarse now, "we Russians with white skin, we're a minority, that is why we fear the Chinese. Oh yes, fear. We see them as clever, industrious automatons like the Germans. To us China is one billion Germans. We are a depressed people. I remember when Nixon came to Moscow we took him to see the grave of the war dead. When he went to Peking the Chinese took him to look at acrobats. You've seen the Kremlin, it is on top of a hill like a fort. It *is* a fort. Once there were forts all over Russia to protect the villages, the *mir*. The Russians went from the *mir* to the metropolis in one jump. That is why we have had such *symashedshii,* such madmen, because we are tortured by perpetual doubt and ambivalence. So our madmen, like yours, dream of the apocalypse. Our monsters and yours locked in a grand *folie à deux,* plotting the *holoca,* the *vnichtodjenia,* the end of the world . . ."

"So you too fear them?"

"I especially, my *lubov.*"

"What do you mean?"

"I am a Jew. Didn't you guess? . . . And now I am going to tell you about the real China Card and your Dr. Manheim. Sit back, dear one. We know that the opening card on the table in 1971, when Dr. Kissinger made his 'secret' visit to Peking, was a complete set of U.S. satellite reconnaissance photos of Soviet troop and missile placements along the Chinese border. Combined Sino-American intelligence has escalated steadily since that meeting thirteen years ago. Dr. Manheim, I am happy to say, had quit the Kissinger group, by 1971 but he did accompany Dr. Brzezinski to Beijing in 1979 to sign the also 'secret' weapons systems agreement.

"All of this, of course, is part of the PRC master plan to get a political commitment from the U.S. and NATO. This is what they want, *not* tactical missiles of their own, they want an American umbrella and Dr. Manheim is unfurling it for them and that has emboldened them to *provoke* a U.S.-USSR confrontation—which has been their goal for decades. That is why the right-wing elements in West Germany began making noises on the side of the PRC as soon as the U.S. gave them nuclear missiles, at which point they offered to cover for the Americans in the event of a clash outside of Europe. The Americans are using you, feeding you news leaks as a diversion while they plan a surprise attack somewhere else—"

"What are you trying to say? I can't follow—"

"I'm telling you that your Wolf, as a child an inmate of a Nazi death camp, is up to his elbows with former Nazis in this China Card game—let me finish. Your Wolf also knows what no one knows outside of a small handful of power managers in Moscow, Beijing and here in Washington."

He stood, heaved his shoulders up and stretched his neck to relieve the tension. As he crossed around the head of the table to approach her chair, she stared again at the abstract art display ten yards away. Her heart was beating fast; without warning the hidden city of bomb shelters in Beijing materialized out of the random construction facing her. As she turned to stare at Arbatov she remembered again that while she and Wolf had viewed life in China's Red Square, the city of death had been beneath their feet, waiting. The Russian sat on the heavy table, angling toward her to speak in the rich, soft tone that was so persuasive to women and diplomats alike.

"You see all this talk of China being as 'invincible as a winged tiger' who presses now for 'an early and decisive war' is not as new as the world thinks. We *know* that the China Card is an invention of the Dulles brethren; that, unknown to Eisenhower, the CIA began in the late '50s to conspire with China against the USSR, and the coin used was thermonuclear . . . Your Wolf was not part of that but he *knows* about it. So much for U.S. neutrality . . . Now you perhaps understand why we moved so quickly for détente with President Kennedy. After his assassination and through the 1970s, despite the bombing of Vietnam, the USSR pressed unremittingly for SALT and détente without, of course, ever giving up for one minute our belief in the laws of the class struggle. We said it openly.

"But after the 1980 election the China Card was slammed down against us on two fronts. We have been pushed to the wall, encircled, driven partly mad—I admit it. And so the Politburo has stated, in secret session, Lenin's dictum—'If we have to go, we will slam the door so that all the world shall shake.' "

She stared straight ahead into the circling lines captured in the vortex of the photo display. She felt his heavy hand touch her shoulder lightly. *"Lubov,* it is true that I am envious of this Manheim. That is stupid but human. But I swear to you that I believe what I have told you to be true. And if Manheim will listen to you —because he loves you as I do, always will—then you must convince him that he is about to make the whole damn world one unending death camp. If you love him then you must confront him with the truth. And that is why I now tell you that Wolfgang Manheim was not the child of Dr. Walter Manheim the Jew and Comintern agent, but instead the illegitimate son of Colonel Ernst Hoder of the Nazi Luftwaffe . . . Whether any part of him knows this or not, the words on *your* lips may shock him into clarity about the holocaust that he is, actively or passively, about to act out . . . Wolfgang's real father, Hoder, was a German aristocrat, later an officer, who had a long affair with Wolfgang's mother. She was a doctor, too. Her *husband,* Walter Manheim, was our agent. Manheim arranged for the boy, Wolfgang, to remain in Berlin even though he was a marked man himself as an important Communist. Then the mother died, but that's not clear. You see . . . *I* am the Jew. Manheim is only a German."

"This is true?"

"Yes. We also know that Manheim suffers from epilepsy. Did you know that?"

"I knew that he has . . . headaches, spells—"

"He is a victim of those camps. I pity him, but I will stop at nothing now . . . and if you can't force him to change or at least expose the truth about the China card, then I can only promise you that we will hold back only until the first American dissidents succumb to their hunger strike. Then we will expose the great Manheim, the *velikiy chelovek,* as an epileptic, the son of a Nazi officer, *anything* to break him and destroy American credibility! Then if the students and activists in Washington and the other capitals of the West rise up—and I mean arson, sabotage, massive and violent disruptions—the USSR will go before the United Nations and pledge to begin real disarmament talks. That will be *our* ultimatum. This is what I will risk everything for with the Politburo . . . Do you love him enough to try?" he asked softly. She nodded, not trusting herself to speak out loud, and rose unsteadily as he straightened the suede coat on her shoulders.

"*Dousha,* if we get out of this, I will be waiting for you. Don't say anything now."

Outside the snow had stopped at last, but a wind was rising as she walked the white streets. "I am afraid I'm going crazy," she thought. "I am being made into a conduit between these two men, but I am being torn apart by them."

Again, like another icy gust of wind, the thought wracked her that it was just possible that Andy Kott alone, and not Wolf, had been the moving force behind using her as a courier to deliver the so-called Wise Men's plan to the Russians. Even that the entire transaction might be a covert charade of some kind. Had she for the first time in her career been compromised, and hopelessly so?

She felt as if she wanted to be sick, to purge herself of all the plots that had become her diet.

She stumbled on against the rising wind, but in her mind's eye she saw only the subterranean streets of the Forbidden City.

January 26, 1984

EVIDENCE OF SOVIET
UNREST REINFORCED
BY OFFICIAL TRIPS
BY
B.J. RUSSELL

WASHINGTON—Top Communist Party officials have made an unusual number of visits in recent weeks to industrial cities of eastern Russia and Siberia, where there have been reports of food shortages and labor unrest, a review of leadership travel shows.

Although the visits do not prove that the reports of strikes and other forms of labor unrest in the provincial cities are true, the analysts said they find the coincidence intriguing.

Such leadership visits could be part of an official campaign to pacify the population in areas where dissatisfaction is believed to have reached unacceptable levels, Western analysts have speculated.

In addition to high-level visits, the sources said, the pattern in the past has been to release food from secret reserves stored in key areas around the country as a response to economic unrest.

The Soviets have denied that work stoppages have taken place, but the Western analysts said those denials

(Please turn to page 19, column 1)

193

January 26, 1984

MOSCOW CALLS U.S. A-STRATEGY 'INSANITY'
BY
B.J. RUSSELL

WASHINGTON—The Soviet Union assailed America's new nuclear strategy Monday as an act of insanity conceived by persons "who have lost all touch with reality and are prepared to push the world" into a nuclear war.

The attack by Tass, the official Soviet news agency, came shortly after more restrained expressions of concern over the strategy by G. A. Arbatov.

Claiming that "mounting waves of war hysteria are sweeping the White House," Tass said that "things are now far more serious because the President has forcefully sanctioned the nuclear strategy—begun four years ago in tentative fashion—whose essence is the threat of striking a first blow at military installations in the Soviet Union."

MILITARY TARGETS GET PRIORITY

The U.S. strategy, now official, puts priority on attacks against military targets in the Soviet Union rather than on cities and industrial complexes, thus making nuclear war thinkable—even, some say, inevitable. National Security Adviser Wolfgang H. Manheim like former Secretary of State Muskie, has revealed that he was not briefed on the decision. . . .

One wonders who is speaking for whom.

16

BOHEMIAN GROVE, CALIFORNIA—JANUARY 26, 1984
(THURSDAY)

"By the banks of the Russian River," Andy Kott muttered, as the limousine carrying the National Security party sped along, well above the speed limit.

"You should see the Grove in the summer," Peter Wick said, pulling rank as usual.

Wolf Manheim had said nothing for most of the ninety-minute drive up from San Francisco through the rich farmlands. The weather was in the high 60s, the sky flecked with a light cloud covering, the air in Sonoma County was still fresh and all of it only heightened the tension he felt. Wolf caught glimpses of the fertile countryside flowing past the half-curtained windows of the official Cadillac. He looked out as if through the eyes of B.J. Russell, remembering her as she had looked in Beijing. He thought of her face and body as he saw from the corner of the curtained window the passing orchards, vineyards, and dairies, the wineries and apiaries; the stands of prize cattle and the fat sheep of the Basque shepherds of this region of northern California. Soon they would reach the great Sequoia forests, nature at her most powerful.

Two of his own Secret Service vehicles passed, each honking once, but James Jarrell, in the front seat on the other side of the bulletproof partition, continued to talk into his radio.

Off to the left, Wolf knew, were the coastal waters teeming with salmon and Dungeness crab, mussels and oysters and abalone— would B.J., not invoke even the fish-filled sea against him if he failed in his mission today?

A battered sign announced that Guerneville was fifteen miles north. Here, a hundred years ago, fur trappers from czarist Russia had once hunted the sea otter, naming their trading town Sebastopol and its meandering river the Russian. Another backup car cut in front, signaling to Jarrell, apparently.

Wolf let the curtain slip shut and turned to look at his two aides. Wick was absorbed in checking a series of documents spread out on the jump table that had been used as a travel bar by the previous occupant of the $175,000 automobile. Andy Kott looked away quickly as Wolf turned toward him; though they had never discussed it in so many words, both of them were a little afraid of Wick, who Kott, though not Wolf, believed was the man on the Manheim staff closest to the CIA. If he was, in such a crisis as they now faced, Wick could have been activated and be reporting directly to A. D. Winston, CIA Director of Operations—the hawk's hawk who was awaiting them at Bohemian Grove.

Wolf did not need to meet young Kott's eyes to know what he was thinking. En route from Washington, on *Air Force Two,* Kott had expressed his deep private misgivings to Wolf, suggesting to him that they should not be flying to the brass and CIA at Bohemian Grove in the middle of a redwood forest in California. " . . . Wolf, why are *we* coming to *them?* Why didn't the Joint

Chiefs send someone who was already in Washington to meet with us? And why is it so necessary for CIA to have Winston fly out here, too? And no one is talking to the President, they seem to want to stay as far from him as possible. Why couldn't we have—"

"Andy, relax, they wanted strict security."

"What's wrong with the War Game Room in the Pentagon? I'm telling you that there is something very wrong in our flying out to this Bohemian Grove . . ."

Not only was that the hardliners' turf, he said, but he had always believed that the Grove had been one of the settings where the assassination of President Kennedy had been plotted.

Wolf had simply stared into the round, intelligent face, measuring the strain of the youngest, up to now the wisest and most certainly the most loyal of his aides, Andrew Bronislav Kott. The assassination of President Kennedy was absolutely never referred to, in conspiratorial terms, in senior government circles. That Kott should even raise the subject was a dramatic signal that the man was on the verge of resignation. (. . . That's what B.J. was after me to do, wasn't it?)

He had told Kott, for whatever reassurance it might be worth, that the retreat had been the site in 1942 for President Roosevelt's most secret S-1 Committee meeting to plan the crash development of the atomic bomb. There Ernest Lawrence, Julius Robert Oppenheimer, James Bryant Conant and Arthur Compton had set in motion the Manhattan Project. "I guess then," Andy Kott had said with a grim smile, "it's quite appropriate." . . . Wolf flexed his long fingers and forced himself to breathe deeply, trying to unravel the ball of fear inside him.

The limousine shot through the little town of Monte Rio and they were, suddenly, at the approach to the 2,700-acre private preserve known to the townspeople, half-jokingly, as the Kingdom of Bohemia. The oversized security vehicle slowed long enough for Jarrell to snap a few commands to the armed Marine guards stationed under the giant redwoods at the entrance. Wolf cleared his throat. "The subject of the China visit and Hu's meeting with me is strictly off-limits. Don't bring it up. If Winston's people do, I'll handle it. During the presentation I will be calling on each of you for worst, middle, and best case statistics in the event of nuclear hostilities." Wick nodded without looking up. Andy closed his eyes and clasped his hands together. "You both know what we came here to accomplish." Wolf thought and added, "Remember we represent the *President,* the man *elected* by the citizens of the United States, not just the 'Commander-in-Chief.' " . . .

The meeting began promptly at 3:00 PM in the most famed of the Grove's many camps—"Mandalay." Not a bird could be heard this deep in the woods. The huge trees filtered the sunlight. Mandalay could have been an expensive Gulf Coast summer home set down among and dwarfed by the ancient trees. The camp was surrounded by Marines at attention as the conferees climbed the three runs of stairs to the screened porch and entered the living room converted for the gathering. Wolf had changed into a gray wool turtleneck sweater and blue blazer; his aides and the representatives of the joint chiefs and Central Intelligence were in the same suits they had put on that morning in Washington. They looked tired; Wolf Manheim appeared refreshed and in command, as he had intended and hoped to. God knew, he didn't feel it. His height tended to intimidate the military men. A. D. Winston was just as tall, but stooped and jerky in his movements. His face and body were a kind of riot of tics. But he was no fool.

Wolf's eyes swept the improvised conference room as he began speaking without notes. Andy Kott shivered and looked around for the thermostat. Two black Navy mess men served coffee and tea, then withdrew from the house.

Andy Kott's notes for the meeting reflected the names of those present: A. D. Winston, Director of Operations, CIA; W. Manheim, National Security Adviser; General of the Army Victor T.

Kramer for the Joint Chiefs. That was all—no one was representing
the Congress of the United States. No press, of course; no ordinary
citizens, also of course, and not even an aide of the Secretary of
State, and most especially not the Director of the Central Intelligence Agency but instead A. D. Winston, the chief of clandestine
operations. Andy Kott had predicted, and he was now proved
correct, that Wolf Manheim was to be the only civilian at this
highest level of security planners. A. D. Winston did not gather
"intelligence," he ran "operations"; his aide was an Army colonel,
a man who had been with him since Chile. Winston was a GS-18,
a supergrade, the equivalent of a general and renowned for his
erratically brilliant mind. Still, Manheim at the moment dominated
the room. The filtered sun was already slanting through the plaid
curtains and the only sound was Kott's scribbling. No one smoked
or moved as Wolf began.

"General Kramer, General Winston. The President wishes me to
make clear that he does not feel that he can go before the General
Assembly of the United Nations to enunciate American policy in
this crisis without the full support of the Joint Chiefs and Central
Intelligence. Despite the international anxiety caused by the cancel-
lation of his U.N. appearance, the President intends—until you
agree, in *writing*—to refrain from demanding concessions of the
Soviet Union at Sunday's extraordinary meeting in Washington.

"Dr. Kott will now read to you the revised demands as agreed
upon last night by the President and the bipartisan and distin-
guished group of advisers with whom he spent more than four
hours, and with whose names you are familiar."

Andy Kott's voice trembled so that he had to stop and inhale
deeply in order to get through the list. Wolf's face was as immobile
as General Kramer's. Winston's left cheek jerked as if he were
winking in a trick film.

When Kott concluded, he passed copies of the single-page memo-
randum to each of the others. There was no other paper. Wolf's

strategy was clear at once to the other two: they were to be limited to voting the entire set of demands up or down. Wick flicked on the overhead light and the two lamps; outside the sun's rays were failing, lost in the forest.

Winston, as if in pain, uncrossed his emaciated legs. Outside a dog barked. The whole installation was patroled day and night by guards wearing neat green uniforms and leading German-trained attack dogs. When the dogs stopped barking, there was no other sound. Winston adjusted his glasses at the bridge of his nose with one finger. The master spy seemed to be melting into the gloom: his hair and skin, like his clothes, looked gray.

Andy Kott peered out into the disappearing grounds beyond the bare lawns—toward the German shepherd dogs that he feared. Wolf waited for Andy Kott to take his eyes away from the darkening landscape beyond the screened windows.

A. D. Winston did not speak without notes. Instead he had for ammunition a black looseleaf notebook marked TOP SECRET in red. One had to lean forward to catch Winston's soft Virginia accent with its undertone of Scottish inflections. A. D. Winston, Wolf reflected, betraying nothing—the architect of over forty years of "Special Ops." *This* was the man the young Chilean revolutionary should have tried to kill; Winston was *el Descuartizado,* the main creator of the Quartered Man that had come to Chile.

Archibald Delafield Winston, VMI '38. OSS France and China —maimed, decorated, a legend out of the war against fascism. Wolf knew the spymaster's profile, just as the rest of official Washington knew it: a hero behind the lines in Spain; a POW in Austria until, disguised as a Nazi, he led a daring Anglo-American breakout; A. D. Winston, the skinny Virginia kid who could kill or torture with the best of the OSS veterans. Winston in Spain to kill Fascists if Franco let the Germans in, and to wipe out the Communist underground if the Generalissimo did not. Then, when peace came, Winston in Italy organizing anti-Communist riots in the streets. Later,

the coup in Iran, Winston laying explosives in the oil fields. After
that the kaleidoscope of the Cold War: Guatemala, Santo
Domingo, Congo, Cuba, Bay of Pigs, Vietnam and, finally, en-
sconced in glory back at Langley, Winston running the operations
in Chile. Winston, the Quartered Man. A burnt-out case, B.J.
would have said—but, Wolf thought, she would have been wrong.
Winston, the war lover, was not through by a long shot. His maddening drawl was accompanied only by Andy Kott's shorthand
scribbling. Wick sat staring over the head of General Kramer at an
ornately framed photograph of a USC football team, while Kramer
stared at the liver spots on his hands as Winston droned on.

" . . . very well and good, but the Joint Chiefs now have a firm
set of conditions to append to the President's list. Before specifying
these conditions we would like to share with you the estimates from
Central Intelligence that lead, inexorably, to what we hold to be a
minimum set of demands vis-à-vis the Soviets. And, so that there
can be no problem in 'communication'—as has happened in the
past—I will call in Colonel Echeverria to tape-record the balance
of this meeting. Besides accuracy, we believe that the President will
want to lean heavily on these latest estimates which we're about to
give you . . . Since this is going to be lengthy I suggest a five-minute
break while we set up."

Winston fumbled for a cigarette and limped toward the door to
the porch while Wolf walked into the house's interior looking for
the bathroom. The first one he found was small and bare. It would
be July before the summer guests of the Grove began to congregate
in holiday numbers. Then, until October, the redwoods would re-
sound with echoes of "Fight, Fight for Old Notre Dame" and a
dozen other songs and yells from the alumni—the nation's power-
brokers, their managers and their women—housed at "Mandalay"
and "Jungle Camp," "Halcyon," "Poison Oak" and "Cave Man's
Camp."

Wolf rinsed his hands and dried them on his handkerchief, then peered into the mirror. The powerfully planed face that stared back at him was set off by the high-necked sweater, and the light brown hair shone brushed and clean. The broad forehead gave no indication yet of the rising pulse pounding behind the olfactory cortex. He stood motionless, his focus drifting, the face of B. J. Russell supplanting his own reflected image. His lips sounded the word "Betsy," then Andy Kott tapped on the door. The aide's voice was hushed, trembling with what sounded like suppressed hysteria.

"Wolf, they're ready . . . Wolf, will these people follow the President's instructions or not? Are we—"

"Andy, close the door."

"Are we in another Cuban missile crisis situation where Bobby Kennedy had to warn the Soviets himself that unless they gave in that President Kennedy might be brought down by an American military coup? . . . Wolf?" The young man knew, of course, that no matter what the answer was he had played a Bobby Kennedy anyway by giving Betsy the working paper.

"Andy, this is much worse than the Cuban crisis. Today there is no Khrushchev. Worse, now there is a nuclear China."

"Was Bobby Kennedy telling the truth about a coup?"

"I think so."

"Well, is this President backing us, his brain trust, his civilian advisers; or is he likely to go with the brass and the ultras in the Agency? Wolf, do you think we're talking about a state of National Emergency being declared—"

"Andy, slow down. It's not over yet. Let's go back in and hear the bad news."

It was almost dark outside now, leaving A. D. Winston in lamplight and the general in shadows. Wolf sat unbending, trying to force Winston to speak up; the pock-marked colonel kept moving the tape recorder's microphone closer and closer. A bad sign: Winston was reading from clean and final copy.

"It is the concern of the studies by the Central Intelligence

Agency and other defense-community analysts that we are overextended, dependent on, and addicted to cheap foreign imports to supply the energy and other resources that fulfill our needs. This is not new news. It is old bad news.

"Ironically, our stiffest economic competitors are still the two nations we beat in World War II, Japan and West Germany. In the wake of the Vietnam War and Watergate, our government's leadership became ineffective, while Japan's hoarding on world markets caused a shortage of lumber, wood pulp for paper products, and wood. Other nations stockpiled zinc, copper and cotton. The Arab oil embargos in 1973 and again in 1982 hit us like a hammer, but Japan, which imports ninety-nine percent of the oil needed to keep its factories running, bent like a pretzel to meet every Arab demand.

"Canada, too, cashed in on the crisis by forming an international cartel of companies to jack up by seven hundred percent the price of the uranium-reactor fuel she produces. In 1974 socialist Jamaica spearheaded creation of the international Bauxite Association— eightfold price increases. A cartel made up of Chil, Peru, Zambia and Zaire—the Council of Copper Exporting Countries—controls seventy percent of the world's copper production and tripled the price by 1981. Our friends!

"The tin cartel—Malaysia, Indonesia, Australia, Bolivia, Nigeria, Thailand and Zaire—made the price of tin jump nearly threefold by putting export limits on its members. Morocco, virtually a phosphate monopoly unto itself, controls forty percent of the world's supply and has sent the international price soaring.

"The Central Intelligence Agency has completed a scenario for ways an enemy could bring America to its knees: Deny us access to certain rare substances that only metallurgists, chemists and botanists have ever heard of but are essential to the hardening of steel, to making machinery resistant to high temperatures and to the manufacture of electronic gadgetry around which our modern industries, utilities and communications are built. Petroleum is only *one* of these vital materials; it is not even the most important one, and our vulnerability is much greater than the public imagines. The CIA has found that the Soviet Union is already systematically and successfully waging an invisible war against us by limiting our access to such raw materials.

"Consider beryllium. Without beryllium metal alloys, the possibilitiy of space travel does not exist. We have been using *more than one hundred percent* of the free world's total production of beryllium, according to the Office of the Chief of Naval Operations; to get enough we have been raiding our own stockpiles, even though we're still depleted from the Vietnam War. We project that by the year 2000 the U.S. will need nearly four times more beryllium than we use today. Where will it come from?

"Chromite—the U.S. has no mines of its own. For nearly one-fourth of our supply we depend on the Soviet Union. According to our estimates, the U.S. is *more* strategically vulnerable to a cutoff of *chromite* than we are to a cutoff of *petroleum.* The world's largest reserves of chromite are located in Zimbabwe. No more need be said.

"Without niobium, sometimes called columbium, and its cousin mineral, tantalium, we cannot build improved jet or rocket engines. The U.S. has *none* of its own niobium; the USSR is independently possessed of every one of these strategic materials. That includes cobalt, which we have to have for most high-temperature metal alloys and permanent-magnetic alloys. It is the only substance suitable for welding metal to glass—an essential process for our exploration of outer space and deep oceans—but we produce *none* of it. We import more than forty percent of our needs from Zaire. In 1978 troops from the Soviet puppet state of Cuba helped stage an attempted overthrow of the Zairian government in Shaba Province, the mining area that contains sixty-five percent of the world's cobalt supply. The attempt failed, but the resulting disruption of production helped the Soviets, cobalt producers themselves, to triple the mineral's price and to inflict another wound on the American dollar.

"In less than twenty years we will need four times more tungsten. We depend on Brazil, Gabon and South Africa for the managanese we need to make stainless steel and high-octane gasoline, and these nations are now *all* unstable. In the fuselages of high-performance aircraft and spacecraft we use exported titanium alloys. To fuel our rockets we need zirconium, ninety-seven percent of which we must import.

"But the USSR has no such shortages. Their ruling clique of hawks and super hawks sit on top of an empire that is self-sufficient in platinum and *every other strategic resource.* The Soviets have Africa encircled and we, the free world, are left grasping at twenty years' worth of oil left in the Sahara desert! It is 11:59 P.M. for the United States of America—if I may just finish, please.

"We are resource poor, and the goal of Soviet policy is to separate us from key raw materials. Progress, speed, the American Dream, the endless frontier—as we know them—are behind us."

Winston paused to sip from a glass of water, and the colonel used the moment to insert a new tape into the machine. As the general recrossed his legs and pinched his pant crease, Wolf braced himself, almost afraid to learn, as he knew he was about to, whether there would be a more than coincidental correspondence between the hardliner's homegrown ultimatum and the one they had asked him to carry back from China. Winston began again.

"Based on the above, and a complete set of estimates measuring Soviet superiority in strategic weapons systems—which is being handed to the President in Washington at this hour, together with the summary I have just read—the Joint Chiefs and CIA must insist on the following amendments to any demands made on the Soviet Union: One, the agreement of the USSR to a U.N. force being installed in Afghanistan and Ethiopia to insure the neutralization of these countries, which are the victims of wanton Soviet aggression; two, the demobilization of the nearly two million troops now massed on the Soviet-Chinese border, constituting as they do the gravest current threat to world peace; and three, substantial withdrawal of Soviet fleet units from the Persian Gulf, the Gulf of Oman and the Arabian Sea.

"That these conditions be accepted within sixty days by the USSR, or the United States of America and her allies will take whatever steps they shall deem necessary to ensure and organize the peace of the world in bringing to realization the conditions enumerated above. These conditions are in *addition* to the preliminary list that you have presented today, and there is, in addition, a top secret addendum that I will hand to you personally before the dinner break—it is being Xeroxed now . . ."

Andy Kott's chair fell over, banging against the floor, as he stood. No one looked at him. Wolf spoke loud enough for the still-engaged tape machine to record his voice:

"Does the so-called top secret addendum include the immediate or eventual declaration by the President of a state of national emergency, with the suspension of civil liberties? Does it further order into an immediate condition of Red Alert the combined military forces of the United States, worldwide?"

The general recrossed his legs. The colonel pushed the OFF button of the recorder. Andy Kott stood frozen while Peter Wick stared straight ahead. Wolf and Winston peered at each other through the gloom.

"We can go over the actual text together by the early evening," A.D. Winston said.

Winston and Wolf dined alone in the Mandalay dining room at exactly 7:00 P.M. The food was delicious. T-bone steaks broiled rare, pan-fried potatoes, fresh tossed salad, wine, and apple pie. Winston drank plain water—because, as he told Wolf, "I suffer from a progressive and incurable disease—alcoholism. Even after twenty years I'm just one drink away from being a drunk." Nevertheless his eyes were unnaturally bright and his speech somehow heavy.

As they ate, Winston made no reference to the secret addendum, just maddening small talk. Wolf had just had time to scan the addendum and he did not yet trust himself to speak of it.

". . . For example, had the Confederacy gone to war in 1850, it would have won," Winston was saying. "The British economy at that time was dependent on Southern cotton for English mills. The British fleet would have had no choice but to blockade the North as part of a Confederate strategy. John Bull would have had to feed the South and starve the North. But by 1861 it was too late. The English had Egyptian cotton from the Nile Valley and couldn't care less about getting involved in a savage civil war—a matter of timing. Like today. So that's the way it goes . . . Steward, bring Dr. Manheim a liqueur."

Wolf could see that Winston had taken very little food, mainly long drafts of water. His shapeless gray-green suit jacket hung from the narrow shoulders and billowed out from the waist like the clothes of the 1950s. Underneath were shattered limbs, Wolf knew. He was suddenly aware of his own robust, healthy looks—except for the "headaches"—and he felt that if he could just keep talking to B.J. *truthfully,* even that affliction might be outwitted. Winston's voice began to bore in again.

"When you're done, Wolf, why don't we get us a little breath of this night air . . . Well, it's like the man said, 'There is a tide in the affairs of men which taken at the height' et cetera. Right now we have the laser and neutron bomb edge, and Peiping has the bodies. In two or three years—who knows? . . . You read over the addendum?"

Winston pronounced the word bomb as if it were "bum," called Beijing not even Peking but reached back all the way to the empire for "Peiping," and sprinkled his speech with a repertoire of linguistic tricks designed to hold his listener's attention. Perhaps, Wolf thought, this was a way of compensating because Winston's wounds made his movements so stiff and asymmetrical that he almost never gestured when he talked. The epithet *el Descuartizado* echoed dimly in Wolf's mind until he said, "Is this trip-wire strategy really your last word?"

The document had made it clear to Wolf that unless the President somehow went over the heads of the Winstons to the country, then the war trap would be sprung. Winston seemed to have discounted the Chinese in his calculation. Here the "trip-wire" was a contingent of eighteen hundred marines to be introduced on the Arabian Sea on "Day 1" (one day after the sixty-day U.S. ultimatum to the USSR had expired). On "Day 4" the addendum called for four thousand American paratroopers to occupy the Iranian oil fields. The obligatory Soviet response would bring the scenario to "Day 5."

"That's just the light brigade," said Winston. "After they're chewed up by those Soviet monster tanks, the American public will demand a nuclear response—tactical, of course."

"I suspect they would. But then if that's the case, why will it be necessary to have declared a state of national emergency, to round up people and so forth, as your addendum indicates?"

"Because of the minority of protestors who are also militant ... How about that walk?" But neither of them moved. The steward completed clearing the table and disappeared inside the house. Outside, besides the marine guards, Jarrell and his security team could be heard from time to time when a walkie-talkie squawked.

"Wolf, is it because you're a Jew? I mean Uncle Joe is going to retaliate with rockets, out of Syria, against Israel. And you know the Israeli position as well as I do."

"I wouldn't say as well—but I know what they say—'This time we take everyone with us.' "

"That's it. And they mean it."

"So do the Chinese. So do the Soviets. But do we? Do you?"

"You don't like me, do you, Manheim? I mean be honest; we might wind up in the same bomb shelter for the duration. But, hell, man, we went to the same school, only they named yours Buchenwald and mine the rue Cheval Blanc Gestapo interrogation quarters. But I mean we learned the same lesson, didn't we—'never again.' "

"Is that what you learned?"

"We may not always agree, Manheim, but I have the highest respect for your justly celebrated intellect. We're both aware of the crisis of leadership, across the board, in the three major powers . . . Let's get that walk if we're going," Winston said, and started his stutter step around the table and out onto the porch. Wolf followed and, after a word to the guards, within a few seconds the two of them were in the redwoods.

"The 'blackness of darkness.' " Winston's drawl was somewhere behind and to Wolf's left. Which made him remember that Winston had at one time been considered, before he had become an OSS superagent, to be one of the most interesting of the young university critics who had taken up the works of Herman Melville as a glass through which to look darkly at the Republic.

They were fifty yards into the woods now. Spots of electric light from the camp looked no bigger than disembodied eyes of night animals, hanging without orientation in the black. Wolf could feel the earthbulging roots of the giant trees under his brogues. The forest murmur was lower than in ordinary woods. The temperature was in the middle 50s. He traced the swelling root with his shoe. At his elbow Winston spat out, "Permissiveness!" and Wolf could hear him begin to urinate.

"Manheim, what happened to us? How did we go rotten to the core?"

"You're sure that we did?"

"Well, for gawd's sake, Wolf, here we are at Bohemian Grove,

where in the summer the cream of the American ruling class—let's
be a little honest—gets itself dog drunk and fucks everything that
walks between here and the Russian River. Dogs, boys, men, and
whores by the busload from Guerneville and the hick towns. I
mean, boy, this place is the Moose Lodge and the American Legion
pissing contest for the Fortune 500. There's two thousand executives and politicians and generals and mobsters and their sweeties
in here, come July first, raising every kind of hell. I've been here,
I've seen the shows they put on—they make Caligula look like Billy
Graham; people so drunk they have to *crawl* up the stairs to their
Cave Man Camp. They start out with a rite called the 'Cremation
of Care' . . . building a funeral pyre to burn up Care. You can see
the flames for miles. The people in the little towns around here just
shake their heads and roll their eyes until they hear the band strike
up 'There'll Be a Hot Time in the Old Town Tonight'—then they
know that they haven't all killed each other, and their women get
ready again for the yearly call. And I'm talking about the men who
have run this country." Winston's voice had risen out of its rut of
cynicism. Wolf's temples began to thud. Then the spymaster's voice
and speech pattern began to change, subtly at first, until the barely
audible Virginia tributary had become a swollen river of sound. The
voice resonated, cackled, hissed and exploded. Was he drunk?

". . . You know the Company, my little shop, set up the Bilder-
berg Group in the '50s, Billy Black and me. Let me tell you a little
story about Blackie, rest his soul. Great family man, lovely daughter, handsome son, steady wife, Marily, a team player. Well, Blackie
was on the road constantly in the '50s setting up the Bilderbergers
and their conferences all over Europe and acting as liaison to the
Agency and the Council on Foreign Relations—the point was for
us to be able to develop what we called 'agents of influence' in every
major corporation in the Free World. You remember the Free
World, don't you, Manheim? So the only rest Blackie ever used to
get was to come out here for two weeks in the summer and drink

himself into a coma. I used to hold him up, or vice a versa, during the 'Cremation of Care'—I tell you about that? Well, the spirits would sing out to 'Burn Away the Sorrows of Yesterday' and to 'cast your grief to the fires.' One year Blackie went round the bend. I had to drag him away from the others. We stumbled away up one of the Sequoia trails. What he was spitting out was that he, William F. Black IV, was a monster. He wouldn't shut up. Yelling about how when he did get home to Virginia, he would lock his children up and attack them sexually, then he'd bloody the house—the wife, he figured, would lock herself in her bedroom and never come out. Later he'd call in a clean-up crew to wash down the blood from the walls and paint the inside of the house . . . That was it. After that Blackie went on the road again making his rounds . . ."

Wolf breathed in the pure air trying to clear his head of the images Winston had planted there. Then Winston started in again, almost reflectively. "There's a tribe in South Africa, along the Nkotami River, that specializes in hunting of hippopotami. Just before the hippopotamus hunt begins the hunter will call his daughter to his hut and have intercourse with her. According to the tribe's taboo this made him a murderer, and *this* gave him the courage to kill the huge beasts—which they worshipped as totems. After the attack and kill the hunter was considered purged, his honor restored . . . like poor Blackie . . . Later, after both of his children were dead, everybody at Langley found out, but no one said a word."

Hadn't something happened to *Winston's* children? Wolf's head was dissolving (could Winston have sent the Chilean terrorist to kill him?). Then, without warning, Winston's voice sank to an intimate confidence, much closer, less than six feet away . . . "Oh, yes, I've seen it. Start on gin in the morning—I'm talking about vice-presidents and presidents of the board, and of this *country*. There's a Texas billionaire who flys in a ton of bulls' testicles for the July fourth feast. He and his friends cart in the cunts from the Palm

Springs-Las Vegas-Kentucky Derby-political convention circuit. Whores regnant, that's the escutcheon of Bohemian Grove. 'Bohemian!' Ambrose Bierce and Jack London, in their time, were club pets and drank themselves senseless here. 'Bitter' Bierce was my kind of writer and, I suppose, London was yours—an opportunistic ignoramus . . ." Winston seemed to be talking in tongues—one moment raving like a red-neck lifer, the next expatiating like the literary critic he had once fancied being.

"Most of the help are queer—'flashing' and fighting all night around the kitchen. It's boys together."

"To each his own, Winston . . . I think we had better get back if we're going to discuss—"

"Oh yes, the chairmen of the board and the house boys and the girls from Guerneville—"

"A.D., you've been avoiding the one . . ."

The silence closed in on them again like a fist. "Winston," Wolf spoke above the pounding of the pulse in his head, "why are you saying all this to me? Of all times, when we're—"

"Because, Manheim, there is no such thing as tactical nuclear strikes not escalating into a *strategic* all-out firestorm within twenty-four hours. You and I know it, the President knows it, the brass know it, and the men who pay their salaries, and our salaries, know it. And the Chinese, bless their million-man frontier divisions, know it too. I just say out loud what they're all thinking— let it come! Let it come and wipe out this goddamn human race. Human, that's rich, isn't it? Let Nature try again."

"Winston, you're certifiable, you sound like something out of a Berlin cabaret in the '20s—"

"You ought to know, Jew boy. We went to the same school, am I right? You saw it in the camps, too. Man—the animal that's red in fang and claw ready to crap on the whole world to protect his lousy 'territorial imperative.' "

Wolf spun in the dark wanting to get the twisted neck between his hands, to stop the cackling of this horribly cynical nihilist. He scraped his hand hard against the rough bark of a tree and the quick shot of pain slowed him down long enough for him to remember that Winston was like a wounded animal, a crazy animal, a patriotic monster made in the service of his country and that he, Winston, *wanted* Wolf to kill him.

"Winston, listen to me," he said, thinking of B.J. and entering farther than he wanted to into Winston's vision in the hope of reaching him, "if we go we take all the other animals down too . . . and these trees, with their growth rings of thousands of years. That's what you're forcing me to tell the Russians. Do we have the right to take *everything* down just because we couldn't learn to—"

"We have to, because we are a poisoned species. If I didn't say these things tonight, when *would* I say them? Of course I'll say them in the blackness of night to a Jew that the President—in a showdown—would consider crazier than I am. That's rich—the jet-set, moving picture star super statesman—the poor Jew who hasn't figured out that the President already knows more about Chinese intentions than he does—thanks to me—who doesn't even know that the President has already signed off on a plan to assassinate Georgi Arbatov and other strong men in the Soviet Politburo. What did you expect him to do when you told him what the Chinese want—even though I'm sure you advised against Hu's view of the situation. He's already given the green light to plant bacteriological lodes inside the USSR—while you're stalling them for sixty days with your song and dance. You didn't think Sang Hobang's mansion in Beijing would be bugged while you were there, either, did you? Your President came out of this Grove. Oh, he'll go along, all right. He's got balls. Not like me. I really don't have any. The Gestapo buried them somewhere in the backyard of the Wilhelmstrasse house . . ."

Winston had thrown down the real China Card, and his voice

had cracked sadistically at the mention of rigging the Hu talks. "Don't take my word for it. Go back and raise the roof, and if we don't kill you maybe you'll get some of your SS heavyweights to kill me and mine. It's been done before—go ahead, do your worst, Manheim!"

He could hear Winston crashing away through the underbrush like the dying animal that he was, heard his call to the guards and the slam of screen door to the porch before the silence closed in again.

The barely audible night sounds were a rhythmic accompaniment to the beating in his head. He willed himself to grasp onto, to cling to B.J., to summon up love to cancel out the craziness revealed in the dark by a southern drawl.

Images began to rotate. He felt his way to a tree and gripped at the rough hide of the red giant. "To each his own," he mumbled. He almost fell at the sound of the police dog barking somewhere in the blackness, even though he was trying not to confuse this camp with the guards and dogs of Buchenwald. Here there was one irreducible rule—even printed on signs in front of each camp— "NOTHING DONE NOR NO WORD SPOKEN HERE CAN EVER BE REVEALED," and they were serious. At the other camp, Buchenwald, the *un*written rule was equally binding—his father had told him, *"You will live so that you can tell the world the truth of the death camps."*

Winston had, of course, exaggerated. The Grove's battle-scarred soldiers and executives walking the lavish grounds saw themselves as philosophers or, at least, ideological kings, but the Grove could not be the hell that Winston had conjured up—busloads of whores dressed up like in a Gestapo brothel. Winston, that devil, had been playing with him, using his psychological warfare to prey on his mind, to flood his nervous system with panic so that he too would give up and opt for death, forget B.J. . . .

He half fell against the huge tree, breathing through his mouth, thinking, Don't let Jarrell and the SS find me like this . . .

The cries from the Buchenwald brothel sounded louder by night than those of the tortured during the day. At first the boy was frightened.

"The brothel is only for the SS and the nonpolitical inmates," Dr. Manheim had told him. "The SS set up the brothel in order to tempt the underground leadership and cause jealousy, corruption. But what the SS planned for us is what happened to them. For us there will never be sex or love again on German soil. To the poor *Luftmenschen* here at the hospital who will never get out of here alive we give tickets or passes. Do not talk to these men. They are already dead."

His father's orderlies in the camp hospital had told him what to watch for, and he had seen some of the things that went on in the hospital between the SS and their special women. But about the wife of the camp commandant, Ilse Koch, he was told in detail by the smooth talker Kurt Titz, the frau's orderly and an important spy for the boy's father and the underground.

"Well, comrades!" The boy had heard Uncle Kurt begin to the circle in the orderly room who let the boy stay for once. "As soon as the children leave for school she gets up, washes, then lies back down on her bed in the nude. Then I bring her her coffee and right on my heels the captain, Handsome Waldeman himself, makes his morning appearance, to be followed in two hours by Colonel Florstedt. Once she had the two of them together and once Florstedt's aide was called in *and* the dog—"

The boy could not understand everything because the men laughed so hard ("To each his own!" they shouted). The boy knew that Frau Koch had her own riding hall and that the walls were surfaced with mirrors and that, according to Uncle Kurt Titz, the grooms and women did everything in front of those mirrors but ride horses. Forms half-horse, half-human rolled past the mirrors of the boy's mind. He had smelled the riding-hall scent as he passed, and heard the band inside playing circus music from their raised platform.

The boy also knew about the isolation barracks for celebrities deep in the woods, opposite the SS residences. Parties were common there, too. "Orgies," according to Uncle Kurt. Dr. Manheim told the boy to discount fifty percent of everything Uncle said except when he told about the Germans, and then the boy should add fifty percent.

Then there was the groom Willi, humpbacked with a face like an angelic urchin, a crude little character, but kind to the boy. Willi told him how once at the stables Master Sergeant Rieger pissed in the champagne glass and Frau Koch and the others drank toasts with it. "Frau Koch!" Willi would yelp. "Ach, that Koch—that ex-stenographer, she bathes in Madeira wine, Sergeant Schmidt told me. She is massaged with lemon juice every day, that's what makes her tits stand up, Schmidt says. Ach, my Koch . . . so you're standing up too, little Wolfie. Come here let me tell you what the Koch would do to you . . ."

The boy had seen the high-ranking SS luxury villas and gardens on the south slope of the Ettersberg where slave labor had constructed fine wooden homes with spectacular views of the Thuringian countryside. The foundations of the villas had been dragged by the Jews up the steep grade, stone by stone from the death quarry. The boy sometimes delivered medicine inside this restricted district and when he told his father some of the things he saw and the way the people, men and women, looked at him, Dr. Manheim told him that, "Sex is a function of food."

The boy knew that among the regular inmates of the slave barracks, two hundred a day died or killed each other in the savage struggles among naked bodies that took place there every night. The boy saw the aftermath of these ghastly scenes and how different naked bodies look from each other depending on whether or not one had died of starvation. Maybe that's what the doctor had meant about food and sex: Each night ravenous prisoners, fresh in from the death shipments, would tear out the electric wires as soon as food slop containers were sent in and a melee in the dark would follow. The politicos had no way of controlling those who knew that they were marked to die. The doctor explained to the boy why they could do nothing for these men, or their women who were sent to a satellite camp where the boy saw them lying in filth, maltreated by women guards who helped supply Frau Commandant Koch with human skin for her lamp shade endeavors. He also heard Uncle Kurt say that not one woman inmate had ever had a menstrual period.

The boy saw other young women who were kept well fed and medicated. These unfortunates were accused of "race defilement," that is, the boy was given to understand, they had "consorted" with Polish men who had been sent to Buchenwald simply because the Nazis had confiscated their properties. The Poles were hung. The women who consorted had their heads shaven and their bare buttocks lashed—the boy actually saw this merciless striping taking place. Afterward these healthy country fräuleins became the private stock of the guards and were always seen at the eating and drinking sprees every month where the tables groaned under meats and sausage plates and wines from France and the Netherlands. The boy watched the feasts, in the open air, in July and August—until all lights were doused, and what he heard there gave him one of his now worsening "spells."

The boy saw and smelled and heard many unpleasant things while on his daily round of medicine deliveries, but still he was willing to go out of the hospital whenever he could because of the operations which Dr. Pfister, another of Frau Koch's suitors, and Dr. Neumann from the Institute of Hygiene of the *Waffen SS,* performed on Jews and some of the women without anesthetic. When Dr. Neumann's approach was telegraphed through the underground, Dr. Manheim always tried to send the boy out into the camp streets on an official errand, though the streets were hardly safe for a child, even if the protective eyes of the underground were always on young Wolfie Manheim.

He had seen full-bodied young German women, too, who were not the property of the camp. As the prisoners from the quarries and the walking dead, the *musselmen,* were marched back to camp past the local office buildings and factories, the boy saw these women run to the doors and windows to point at the freaks and madmen. And how the SS preened and strutted, as they kicked and whipped and punched the slaves for the benefit of the fräuleins. Then the women would make certain gestures to the walking skeletons that the boy, somehow, understood. They lifted their skirts above their knees, swaying, showing their white legs and hips, their white undergarments; gesturing to the boy, too, until he ran away.

But at night, often, from the hospital, the boy would hear the raucous shouts and laughter from the brothel and he could not sleep. Tickets for the brothel were dispensed only at the hospital, and only to nonpoliticos. Once the boy asked if he could just go and look and his father had slapped his face, but not hard. With the suddenness of the slap the boy had been made dizzy by a fantasy so vivid and oppressive that he had to sing "To Each His Own, To Each His Own," over and over again to himself. Nothing, however, no matter what, would blot out this living picture crawling around inside his head like the rats in the mirror-lined stables: the blinding mirage of his mother nude in the brothel, open to the inmates and the SS. He thought that he could hear *her* laughter mingling every night with the oaths and screams. No, that was impossible, he kept repeating, because he had attended his mother's funeral in Berlin. But why had her coffin been closed? Was it possible that . . . "To Each His Own, To Each His Own." Impossible and yet . . .

"This is the Bohemian Grove . . . not the same . . . different police dogs . . . must get out . . . get to Betsy." His mother's face and hair merged with Betsy's—both blond, both large-eyed and full-lipped.

He straightened, still touching the tree with his right hand. He wanted to pray that he was over the crisis of the *petit mal* for tonight.

Then he remembered A.D. Winston, and the Spanish general who cried "Long Live Death," and Betsy's love and grief, and he saw Betsy's body in his mind's eye, saw her long legs and dimpled dancer's buttocks, her field of pubic hair sloping down to the pink vestibule—and then, clearly, he knew that he must make a child with this woman. Resign, say no to the President, say no to Him, go far away with Betsy and make a child. He rubbed the trunk as if for luck and turned back toward the lights from Mandalay.

As he stepped off, James Jarrell spoke almost point-blank into his face—"Mr. Winston was worried about you." They faced each other in the dark, then the SS man turned and flicked on a flashlight to trace the path.

Wolf took his time, his heartbeat slowing, thinking—"Jarrell *is* Winston's man on my staff, and there must be others—Wick must have been in on it for Winston to have information like this on the Chinese plan—but they can't stop us from getting away, not with all their dogs, human and canine." (By "us" he was thinking no longer only of himself and B.J-R. but, in the last five minutes, their child.)

"Jim," he called from the porch, "patch me in to Washington on secure voice. And get that cryptographic officer up here with the key-cards for the Chinese diplomatic code. I want to leave in two hours for Andrews. That is correct. We leave here at midnight, California time. Where's Andy Kott? Wake everyone up."

17

BOHEMIAN GROVE, CALIFORNIA—JANUARY 26, 1984

(THURSDAY NIGHT)

"Miss Russell—operator, my name is Andrew Kott, K-O-T-T, that is correct. Miss Russell, I'm sorry I had to call collect, I know it's almost four in the morning Washington time but I had no choice . . . Thank you. I'm in a telephone booth on the highway at a crossroads . . . Hello? . . . Miss Russell, I must once again ask you to do something for me. Would you please call my wife and tell her to take the child and go at once to her parents' home in Texas. Tell her that I will try to meet her there. Wait—don't use the phone . . . my home phone—oh, my God, your phone, *the phone you're talking on now must also be tapped.* . . .

"Forgive me, Miss Russell, I'm very upset, I . . . Peter Wick just tried to kill me. I said, Peter—no, I got away. No, Wolf is on the plane, back to Washington. Warn him. No, there's no time—take

221

a car to my house, it's the last one on Beekay Court, 1142, in Vienna, Virginia. Virginia, not Austria. . . . Tell her that . . . yes, thank you, thank you so much. Tell her to take the child and her family to the little fishing village near Guymas, she'll know the place. Tell her not to believe *anything* she hears on the media. Tell her not to use my name on any account. What? Yes, there may be a nuclear alert within twenty-four hours; if not there will certainly be a state of National Emergency announced. I said there will be . . . yes, that's correct. I'm sorry to talk so fast but two guards shot at me after I broke away from Wick. Tell Wolf that Wick is Winston's man too. What? No, Wolf knows nothing about what they tried to do to me, I don't know what they've told him—probably that I've gone crazy but . . . oh, thank you, thank you for saying that . . . What? No, just my leg . . .

"Listen, Miss Russell, tell my wife to forget about any shelters in this country—get to Mexico, tell her, tell her *not,* not to follow the instructions about coming back outside and washing away radioactive particles. Tell her there'll be no more than a fifteen-minute warning, so she's got to take the child and go *now.* Tell her to fly and then drive day and night and not to stop for anyone . . . my little girl Halina . . . forgive me, give me a minute to . . . I'm sorry. Tell her that they should continue to drink water and to eat lightly —I beg your pardon? . . . No, Mexico, forget it, there has *never been* a successful emergency drill. That's . . . no, I . . . yes, that is correct, Miss Russell. I want—wait a minute, I think I hear someone—

" . . . Hello, no it's all right. Can you hear me? I'm afraid I've been shouting and someone might—yes, all right, can you hear me now? There's much more worked out than merely the ultimatum that the Chinese are waiting for Wolf to get. I've found out the Order of Battle, the OOB, that's why Wick tried to—be careful of him, he's—he has no children . . . I'm sorry, I'm sorry, I'm going to pieces . . . "

"Andy, Mr. Kott? You *are* hurt, aren't you? . . . Of course, but if you could just slow down and speak a little louder. Yes, go on, I'm writing:

. . . windowless blue three-story cement bldg next to freeway north of San Francisco—command center for U.S. Air Force satellites, and laser and particle beams—

"Louder, Andy, there's a bloody fleet of helicopters here . . . Yes, go on."

". . . reason had to go Cal is becz Gen. Kramer in charge Cal secret center—also meeting place deserted so could KILL WOLF & K . . . center is key link in U.S. capability to fight war in space. Worldwide network tracking stations that control hundreds of military satellites—"Ferrett" satellites gather photographic electronic intell and relay to Satellite Control Center. Soviet anti-satellite vehicle Cosmos 117—U.S. killer satellite designed to close Cosmos to within hundred yards. Amer killer satellite carried by F-15—70 percent Amer military communications routed through space—K says Pentagon plans do battle with USSR in space while China's conventional forces cross western borders into USSR—

"Andy—Mr. Kott, I can't hear you, there's a—is that a dog? . . ."

" . . . Hello. This is Russell of the London *Times.* Will you please inform Ambassador Arbatov that . . . Russell, R-U-S-S-E-L-L . . . yes, he will be expecting—Hello! Hello Georgi—thank God . . ."

" . . . *Da,* I'll take it—Hello (it's all right), hello Betsy, what is it? No, do not worry, who can sleep? Have you heard that the U.S. Cabinet has departed *en masse* for Camp David? No, what? . . . from California, from Manheim? . . . Anyway, what did your source say? . . . I believe it. It's true the President is almost senile, and weak, terribly weak by now. We have a report, confirmed by our

Salyut overflights, that a South African team is testing 155-Howitzer rocket-launched tactical nuclear weapons off the coast of South Africa—has been testing all this week. An American general named Kramer has just returned from the Cape—what? . . . Kramer, yes, it has to be the same man, that is correct. He uses Air Force cover but he has been a CIA supergrade since the 1950s . . . Do not ask me, dear one, Moscow Center keeps me on the line hours at a time screaming demands—I don't know what to think. The Americans won't let us alone, we have no life, no life at all— only war, war and preparation for war. Just before your call we received a secret signal that West Germany has begun mobilizing elite units around their new nuclear installation outside of Bremen. Moscow Center puts this together with the South African eruption and declares that it is *Remdvenko Kasowa*—a Red Alert . . . Ask your Wolf about the little games of zero-sum in the Pentagon War Game Room, please ask him . . . Betsy, what can I tell you? The sick old man dreaming away at Camp David still thinks that it is the 1950s and that he is presiding over the Great National Barbecue —I am using your most apt phrase. I am not Gromyko, I am not mincing words. We will not back down again, it would be fatal. No, no, you don't seem to realize that the U.S. *has* no competitive army, it only has *nuclear* weapons . . . and the Chinese have no nuclear *credibility,* they have only armies . . . "

" . . . yes, I know we can't go back, but why are you agreeing with Moscow Center about 'this time we will—' . . . You're tired, Georgi, I can tell—please, give me some credit, I know you, you're beside yourself . . . Listen, Georgi, seize the moment—*you* go before the U.N. Be a *real* Machiavelli for once. What do you think would happen if the Kremlin announced a general stand down—I'm talking about pulling troops and armaments back, a *little,* in Europe and Asia. Take away what you consider the pretext for the American hawks, and the group controlling this country would virtually collapse economically and politically—Visionary? Well, . . . that's what I . . .

" . . . Georgi, you're twisting my words. I said the same thing would happen if the Americans had the sense to threaten you with a limited but dramatic stand down—You know bloody well that you're as hooked on the nuclear narcotic as the Yanks. Look, at least you could call for those U.S.–USSR demonstration blasts in the Pacific so the world could see again the destructive firepower behind all the he-man rhetoric . . . What? . . . I know, I know all about it, Georgi, but that is *past*. Stop being the mirror image of what you hate in the West . . . I'm not talking about *unilateral* disarmament, I'm talking about a few *modest* gestures of sanity . . .

" . . . I-am-talking-to-you-on-this-telephone and I don't give a damn if the combined secret services of the world are plugged in —tell them they have to begin disengagement and call it victory . . . You're *giving in* to paranoia. Georgi, there are other traditions in Russia besides paranoia—you taught them to me—but you are betraying your revolution by using the corrupt weapons of the past . . .

" . . . No, I understand . . . Listen, Georgi, real people with real lives . . . I know, I know, but *someone* has to say it—*whoever disengages first wins!*

" . . . Yes, yes, I *will*. I'll get down on my knees to him but you have to— All right . . . go to *your* game room now and, goddammit try, and Georgi—remember when you read to me from Gorki, in front of the fireplace in London . . . there will come a time when each will be a *star* to the other and when . . . I know, I'm at the absolute end of my tether, I have to get out to Virginia now and tell the family of my source in California that their loved one wants them to run for their lives . . . Yes, I have to go too . . .

"*Remember* me, Georgi . . . Georgi, don't ring off, I'm terrified, I beg you not to, Georgi . . .

" . . . Hello, I need a cab immediately. My name is, excuse me . . . my name is Russell . . . (As if that matters) . . .

18

WASHINGTON, D.C.—JANUARY 27, 1984
(FRIDAY MORNING)

Arbatov squeezed his eyes tight shut, opened them to stare at Mr. Ulan. Gregory Alexandrovitch Ulan sat stiffly with the telephone receiver a few inches away from his small foxlike ear. Arbatov could hear a far mechanical echo of her voice calling—"Georgi!" —then the click of disengagement.

Ulan sat immobile glaring straight ahead at the avant-garde display on the far conference room wall. He squinted at the paintings and graphics then, slowly, he lowered the gray plastic receiver into the cradle, but he did not cease his glowering at the display. Arbatov knew that the things he'd said to Betsy had infuriated Ulan. A bureaucrat who kills by the number, who is beyond ideology, much less compassion, that is how he thought of Comrade Ulan. He could talk as he pleased, Arbatov realized, as long as Moscow wanted him as their dove in Washington. Only that long, he knew, would Comrade Ulan permit him the indiscretion implicit in a relationship with a woman like Betsy Jones-Russell.

Arbatov studied Ulan, thinking: two nights ago—was it?—she was sitting in exactly the same seat and she was frowning at the far wall, too. Except that she is my love, will always be my love, while Gregory Alexandrovitch Ulan has been sent here on behalf of the KGB to take over these "peace negotiations." G. A. Ulan and his circle may suspect the Jew, and call me the Soviet Kissinger but at least they cannot, as in the old days, liquidate me for my tastes in love and even art. Or can they . . . ?

G. A. Ulan glared ahead while Arbatov stared, red-eyed, at him. "Gregory Alexandrovitch," Arbatov began, "it is now half-past three in the morning and this room is very cold. May I suggest that we retire. You must be fatigued after your long trip."

Ulan did not look fatigued. He was built spare and light, less like a Russian bureaucrat, Arbatov reflected, than like an English banker. He looked alert at all times, like an English hunting dog. His eyes were bright brown and would have been his most attractive feature if it were not that they were so light and mottled. Now he looked at Arbatov with the large, light-colored eyes and licked his dry lips before saying, "No. I am not fatigued."

Arbatov rubbed at the eighteen-hour beard on his chin, then ran his fingers through his wiry hair, as though trying to force blood to circulate through his brain. No, Ulan did not look tired, *his* eyes were bright, *his* dirty brown hair was slickly in place on either side of the bare white crown. Even his blue pin-striped suit had somehow kept its crease and drape all day and half the night. Arbatov blew his nose and scratched hard at the hairline around his collar. His skin was beginning to break out in red patches, a product of his fatigue and frustration at every level. Though the same age, tonight Ulan looked ten years younger than Arbatov, the faded hero of Stalingrad.

"This woman—what are her motives? Besides physical atraction, I mean."

The problem with the KGB mind, in Arbatov's opinion, was that like any other secret service it saw a cause/effect universe. Like eight-year-olds, spies were little bundles of secrets. Spies stared at grown-ups and burned with curiosity: What made them tick? Always in search of the motive behind the motive, the blackness at the heart of darkness, the spy/child knew that he did *not* know, really, what it was that men and women did together—that was what drove spies mad, Arbatov believed, they knew that there was something beyond the mechanics but they did not know what it was.

"Would you like something, Gregory Alexandrovitch? Tea? Milk?"

"Milk, please."

"One moment, I will ring . . . Her motives?"

"Yes."

"I am not entirely sure beyond the obvious ones."

"The obvious ones?"

"Yes. Peace, survival . . . You were listening in, you—"

"Yes, I am familiar with her work . . . Are the Americans using her?"

"Using her?"

"Yes. For that matter, can we use her as well,?"

"In what way? Ah, here is your milk, wait, here is a napkin, too."

His ulcer is killing him—Arbatov rubbed his head with his knuckles—at the thought of a real woman like Betsy. I know all about his sexual life, Arbatov realized as he pulled his tie all the way off, I know without knowing anything about it, or wanting to.

Ulan finished the milk and patted his lips. "If you told her certain things would she pass them on to Manheim?"

"What sort of things, Gregory Alexandrovitch?"

"Such as our intentions if the United States refuses to bargain in good faith."

"Perhaps. And what are our intentions, as you understand them, Gregory Alexandrovitch?"

"To wait until your talks with Manheim have stretched into at least March and the important American presidential primaries. The talks will strengthen the hand of the American doves and the Kennedy wing of the Democratic Party. The American hawks will be forced to act in secret unless or until they can elect a warmonger, and that is doubtful based on their disappointments since 1980. Thus, if Manheim can convince the cabinet that, unless the talks continue . . ."

"Convince them of what?"

"We announce the beginning of extraordinary Warsaw Pact maneuvers tomorrow. You could let the Russell woman understand what these maneuvers mean."

"I am aware of the maneuvers but perhaps not of their full significance. More milk,?"

"No, thank you. We are deploying MIG-25s and R-80 battle tanks to the German Democratic Republic . . ."

Arbatov pulled at his hair and then his eyebrows, covering his face with his heavy hands. He'll give *me* ulcers with that electronic voice of his and this talk of secret maneuvers. God in heaven, everybody has known for weeks that there would be special armored infantry and motorized infantry and second echelon armor and the unveiling of the new SCUD missile and all the rest of the motorized and electronic juggernaut to impress the world. *Kiev*-class carriers, elite parachute units . . . what about it?

"I am aware of all this, Gregory Alexandrovitch—"

"Yes, but the American Joint Chiefs must be made aware that this time maneuvers will go on until bilateral agreement is achieved, and that if it is not achieved, then the maneuvers will become— *overnight*—operational."

Ulan pushed the empty milk glass a few inches further away with his fingertips and patted his lips unnecessarily with the still-folded napkin.

"And is this development, of which I have heard nothing before this minute, the truth?"

"No."

"I wonder. But you want the Americans to believe that it is the truth?"

"That is correct, Georgi Arkadyevich. But you are skipping a step. First the Russell woman must believe that it is the truth."

Arbatov sighed and scratched at his chest with both hands and then commenced to rub his wrists. Leave it to a Stalinist to make a stupid plan sound clever, he thought. He yawned with fanfare, then, almost shouting—"And what *is* the truth?"

"The truth, Georgi Arkadyevich, is that no later than 15 February we intend to strike through Mongolia at the Chinese bases in Sinkiang and Singhai. We will, as well, occupy upper Manchuria from the Lesser Khingan Mountains as far as Changhun. Moreover we will occupy the port of Dairen and the Gulf of Chihli . . ."

Ulan had begun to roll the napkin into an irregular ball. Arbatov cursed silently. Ulan's use of the antiquated Stalinesque place-names for the Chinese locations seemed somehow worse to Arbatov than the plan of treachery itself. That and his non-human voice. Despite the chill of the oversized conference room Arbatov began to sweat again. Far away the Washington Cathedral bells tolled the quarter hour . . .

The two men stared past each other, Ulan apparently trying in his mind to enforce order and predictability on the random emergy of the Kandinskys; Arbatov, for his part, seeing superimposed on the blank wall opposite the spectacle of neutron bombs, piled up like a stockade around the perimeter of Western Europe in the fashion of the ancient barricades meant to shield the civilian populations from the Hundred Years' War.

Arbatov began to chew on his knuckles to keep from scratching at his protesting skin. Now, he brooded, Betsy was to be used again as a conduit to make Manheim believe that these neutron defenses in Europe would be the first target. And Manheim would probably be taken in because he, Manheim, had not signed off on Directives 53, 58, and 59—those plans for "pinpoint" and "surgical" nuclear operations of a First Strike that the American hardliners were now leaking behind Manheim's back. Manheim's resentment of being cut out could be played on, and so could Betsy's obsession with her love for life and her desire to urge on both her lovers a sort of surpassing Truce . . .

Arbatov looked at the teeth marks on the back of his hand. And Ulan, he thought—vicious Stalinist sitting here making the moral case for nuclear war—he is our so-called New Soviet Man? Bigoted high priest of state terror meeting his production quota of lies while my children scheme to get their hands on a pair of Wrangler blue jeans. The thought of his children and their present peril made Arbatov bite into his hand again.

"Is this leak from you?" Ulan had fished out a news clipping from inside his perfectly pressed suit jacket and now pushed it across the table.

POLAND'S STRIKES SPREAD
BY
B.J. RUSSELL

WASHINGTON—Industrial unrest in Poland spread Thursday to the manufacturing city of Lodz, posing the most serious challenge to the country's Communist authorities since a wave of strikes paralyzed the country four years ago.

A high Soviet source in Washington speculated today that the Kremlin would follow its 1980 "Everything within the Revolution" policy. According to the official, who refused to be named, if the Kremlin should suspect that "American or Chinese circles" are contemplating playing a "Polish Card" then there would be an

(Please turn to page 4)

"No," Arbatov said, not even looking at the story.

Ulan disregarded the denial. "Well, oil can be leaked as well as water, comrade." Silence again.

"And does the Premier intend to amplify this deception and these leaks over the hot line to the President of the United States?"

"The indications are, comrade Arbatov, that the hot line will not be in use."

"Will not?"

"That is correct."

"And why would the hot line not be in use during the greatest threat to survival we have ever faced?"

"Because the President's adviser will not let him use it. Because he is not—well. Manheim, alone, is the stalking horse for the ultras around the President."

"The President is not well? . . . Is he alive?"

"Yes, of course. But he will be in contact with the outside world only through intermediaries. So forget the President and focus your thoughts on Manheim and the Russell woman."

"When I focus on Manheim I recall that he has returned, only a few days ago, from meeting with Vice-Chairman Hu. I wonder to what degree you have considered—"

"What should be considered is what you and I have just heard from this Russell, that Manheim is currently returning in such a hurry not from a ceremonial meeting with the Chinese but from a confrontation with the extremists in his own government. What do you think this great statesman will do first when his plane arrives in Washington in a few hours?"

The cathedral bells tolled the fourth hour of the new day. Arbatov no longer had the strength to continue rubbing at his erupting skin. He sat, now, with his shaggy head in his hands.

So this is why they have sent Ulan to Washington, he thought . . . to sit behind me, invisibly, during the Manheim talks with an invisible gun at my head. And to see that the American joint chiefs and NATO find out, a little bit at a time, through Betsy, that Germany and Western Europe will burn unless the U.S. stands by while China is punished.

It will not work, Arbatov wanted to scream into the death mask across from him. It will not work because the Chinese will overrun all borders and rocket Vladivostok with *American* supplied missiles. The rest would be automatic. Arbatov knew how the infernal machine would unwind. He could almost hear the clicks inside his aching head: Vladivostok; then Beijing for Vladivostok; then the American's take Minsk for Beijing; then Manchester or Leeds for Minsk; then Moscow or, if it were to go on that long, Washington. The Soviet Order of Battle unrolled in his head—three thousand warheads in a period of six minutes. Soviet SS-9s bracketing Washington. The U.S. response—three thousand retaliatory missiles in twenty-five minutes against two hundred Soviet cities, Poseidon and Trident missiles surfacing from the sea, 113 million Russian casualties, 140 million American—in the first hours, that is. And himself and Manheim screaming into red telephones, staring into dead red telephones, that it was a mistake. High above in a 727, the President of the United States, if he was still functioning, trying, too late, to warn the Prime Minister of Canada . . . Eleven hours later —all phones dead.

Arbatov pushed against his temples. Still, Ulan waited. Arbatov wanted to laugh out loud now, or strangle Ulan. The czarist nightmare of Empire was to find its last avatar on the lips of the last Stalinists, the KGB world-killers. And he was supposed to use the women he had loved, it seemed forever, to start it; he was to throw her onto the wheel of history. And if the wheel did not turn, he was to throw himself on afterward, and then it would turn. Before that moment came, he reflected, the guns at his head (and at those of the other moderates) would no longer be invisible.

Arbatov thought, I will sleep now and when I wake up I will have the strength to kill Ulan, or Manheim, or myself—I will have the strength and the wit to know who must die with me in order to create a firebreak, in order to create an ounce of time for rebellion. I believe in human beings, he thought. They will, finally, rebel for survival.

Out loud he said: "Gregory Alexandrovitch, you are a bachelor, are you not?"

19

BEIJING—JANUARY 27, 1984
(FRIDAY)

The emergency sirens of Beijing did not paralyze like those of Berlin or assail the ears like Washington's or New York's. In Beijing the arc of the sound was broad, it filled space without splitting it, it simply wiped out all other sounds the way an eraser cleans a blackboard, and yet within an hour one could function in an almost normal fashion.

They had filled the sky for twelve hours now and drowned out the million-footed city with its schools, its cars and its buses and the calls of the old people exercising in the parks and by the frozen river . . .

Mr. Hu slept in the Underground City in what could have been a hotel room in Moscow in the 1950s or in America of the 1930s. "Responsible Cadre," like Mr. Hu, were quartered along the four sides of a broad square one hundred by one hundred yards. Mr. Hu's seniority brought him twin beds in a room approximately ten feet by ten. There was a wardrobe, a desk, two chairs and a tea table, three blue shaded lamps, a plant of winter roses. A faded and poor

237

picture of the Pao Ho Tien palace hung over the desk. Piled nine inches high on the same desk were diagramed paradigms of the Underground City, numbered mazes running miles in all directions, stretching from the center of the old city under the Great Wall past Shunhwa nearly to Jehol. Piled neatly next to these subterranean maps was a series of directives and statements from the Ministry of People's Culture. They were in large capital type so that Mr. Hu could read them easily, even in dim light.

Mr. Hu stirred and woke before his orderly could arrive to tell him that it was 10:00 P.M., or hour twelve since the alert began at 10:00 A.M. that morning. Mr. Hu had slept for only two hours in the last twenty-four yet he opened his eyes, recalled where he was and reached to his right toward the adjacent desk for his rimless glasses. Then, his eyes focused, he checked the clock, then stared at the blank plaster wall opposite, waiting for his orderly and seeing there the fading reflections of the dream from which he had just emerged.

Across the dream, scores of boys had been marching along together in irregular ranks. He could not hear what they were singing though he knew, the way a dreamer does, that it was a song of the Long March, and that the boys were the Little Devils of all those years ago, or their ghosts or shadows. The landscape was that of the Plateau of Yünnan. The dreamer knew all this as he reviewed the ranks of sunburned boys in relief against the sky so blue in its purity as to be almost white at the horizon. The boys were hungry looking and clad in poor homespun, yet their teeth flashed white as they sang the soundless anthem. Then the scene shifted without warning to the political prison at Abundance and Glory streets, north of Yünnan in Chungking. Chiang Kai-shek torturers paced the corridors. In mass cells the boys smiled and sang. There was no despair. Then, again, suddenly, the boys were free, striding east toward far Fukien through Changsha province south through Kiangsi—then, at last, Foochow and the East China Sea.

All this taking—in dream time—timeless moments. There they all were, singing and weeping openly at the moment of journey's end. The sea sounded in his ears. It was time: at his back was all of China, before him the white whipping of the Pacific Ocean . . .

Mr. Hu stared dry-eyed at the now perfectly blank plaster wall. Into his hearing the wailing—now in its twelfth hour—crept through the walls. He could not hear the million-footed masses as they climbed down thousands of underground staircases yet, as if in a dream, he could sense their pulse in his. The cold was seeping through the walls, the cold with the siren sound inside it. Mr. Hu shuddered slightly and remembered the Chiang Kai-shek prison and the young Ho Chi Minh. Uncle Ho, fifty years later, had said to Mr. Hu, during the 1970 U.S. bombing of Hanoi—"I have never married and founded a family because I was too occupied in tending to the care of my nineteen million children." Had he been presumptuous?

Mr. Hu rose and opened the locker that stood battered and discolored between the wardrobe and the desk on the north wall of the room. He was shrugging into a quilted winter half-coat when the gangling orderly entered with a batch of communiqués. There was one from the National Security Adviser to the President of the United States, but it was not the one he had been waiting for. And it had come in not by the standard diplomatic code, but in Manheim's own NSC cipher on the radio net of the joint U.S.-Chinese military assistance command, and it asked Mr. Hu to await his next signal.

Aboveground the street lamps burned bright as always. Mr. Hu crossed the almost empty courtyard heading for the Tai Ho Men Gate, the headquarters for evacuation of the central city. Runners with dispatches in their gloved hands hurried over the five bridges toward the rendezvous point at the Gate of Supreme Harmony.

Under the night illumination from the marble balustrades the five bridges seemed to form a belt of jade around the river. This is how the scene inspired Mr. Hu, as he paused waiting for the young orderly. The runners trotted past, they knew who he was and did not tell him to get below. In fifteen minutes the street lamps began to phase out.

Mr. Hu started out again. At the Dragon Pavement the orderly caught up to him clutching a fresh sheaf of coded signals. They strode on, the wind at their backs, the square empty. They passed the Palace Museum, built in the Emperor Chien Lung's reign. Mr. Hu imagined the spectacle of ten thousand men slaving to transport the stones in the dead of winter. The crated stones pulled over a frozen road made with water drawn from wells dug especially for the purpose every five hundred paces. The ancestors, Mr. Hu thought, of those millions who for the past twelve hours had been pouring like giant tributaries through the Meridean Gate across the Forbidden City and down in great waves to their new abode in the underground.

Mr. Hu had watched the multitudes flood past Tai Ho Tien, the Hall of Supreme Harmony, toward the waiting catacombs. And he had been moved as always at the patience and seriousness of the Chinese people. Under the universal sirens they had passed, helping those who were too young or too old to keep pace with the flow. The palace loomed in the dark now, unchanged since its building in 1420, and Mr. Hu thought—"We are many millions yet we are one person, millennia old, spread across the earth. We live and struggle from generation to generation—in the mountains, in the caves, above the earth, beneath the earth. We are one man and one woman."

The orderly caught up with Mr. Hu again at the center of the four towers near the moat that surrounded the Imperial Palace. The moat reflected streaks of illumination but the bare, black trunks of the winter trees melted into the rippling shadows of the windswept

water. Mr. Hu saw the up-shining lights and the bottomless shadows out of the corner of his eye as he tramped toward the Five
Phoenix Towers and the Forbidden City. He imagined, again, his
ancestors stepping on these very stones, turning their heads to the
sound of the bell and the drum issuing from the Towers. Somewhere out of the scope of the warning sirens he could hear the
ancient tintinnabulation of the ancestral bell and drum ringing and
beating out the call for his ancestors to hurry to the Temple of
Heaven and Earth for the sacrificial ceremonies. Mr. Hu passed
where today millions have passed, where yesterday tens of millions
of the ancestors had hurried toward the Temple of Earth.

Mr. Hu had reached the North Gate, Shen Wu Men. He did not
need to look up at the gate tower. He could hear the tolling of the
bell—one hundred and eight tolls marking dawn and dusk—and
the beating of the drum that his ancestors had heard. The same
stones, he thought again, even the same legs—one person-millennia
old.

The orderly rushed past, then stopped and turned, realizing that
Mr. Hu had paused and was staring at the floodlit pile of the
Chairman Mao Memorial Hall. Mr. Hu, himself, along with Chairman Gwa had helped to lay the first stones for the foundation of
the thirty-four-meter-high hall in 1976. Now, Mr. Hu strode forward toward the two tiers of yellow glazed tile cornices into the
shadows of the forty-four octagonal granite columns that formed
the peristyle. The huge tomb drew his stubborn, stocky figure.

They passed through the giant doors of carved *nanmu* wood that
stood on either side of the north hall. The orderly dropped behind,
allowing Mr. Hu to enter first into the central hall where the body
of Chairman Mao lay in its crystal coffin surrounded by flowers in
full bloom. Mr. Hu stopped near the coffin; the viewing aisle was
lined with pine and cypress. The orderly slowly read the words
embossed in gold on the white marble of the south wall—

"ETERNAL GLORY TO THE GREAT LEADER AND

TEACHER CHAIRMAN MAO TSETUNG."

Mr. Hu stepped up next to the coffin. Through the flawless crystal he looked down on Chairman Mao. He studied the firm, serene features, complete even to the red tint they bore in life. His eye took in the immaculately pressed gray uniform, the neatly folded red and yellow flag of the Communist Party of China that draped the corpse. Mr. Hu stood for perhaps a full minute, then turned to the orderly still fifteen yards behind him. His voice sounded weary yet clear as he spoke: "It is time now to move the coffin below. Go tell the memorial personal bodyguard."

The orderly turned and ran out, appearing, to Mr. Hu, truly frightened for the first time. Mr. Hu passed through into the south hall and paused again to read the familiar lines from a poem of Chairman Mao's. The walls of the south hall were decorated with designs of hibiscus and on the white marble in the Chairman's own vigorous and powerful calligraphy were the lines

"AND I AM LOST IN DREAMS, UNTRAMMELED DREAMS OF THE LAND OF HIBISCUS GLOWING IN THE MORNING SUN"

The characters were in the Hunan style, the style of Mr. Hu's childhood.

Mr. Hu lingered for a final time in the east lounge before descending into the underground. He stood in the middle of the brightly lit chamber, without moving, and looked at the paintings and wall tapestries depicting the historic scenes of Chairman Mao's life and of his, Mr. Hu's, past: the snow-topped mountains crossed during the Long March; the date orchard where headquarters had been set up during the Yenan years; the flooding rivers that Mr. Hu and the vanguard of the Red Army had crossed . . .

Then Mr. Hu walked straight out through the far door, inserted a large key into an unmarked, oversized single door of white steel, pushed hard, stepped forward and down onto the wide slate-colored stairs that led below into the subterranean control and communication center.

Beneath the pavement, the last waves of the people of Beijing poured through the special doors in all the official buildings, the department stores, the sports stadia, they poured down.

Most families carried neatly folded blankets, some younger children clutched simple rag dolls or wooden toys. The adults, for the most part, appeared grave yet serene, as if this descent had long been expected.

The temperature in the underground city was at least ten degrees colder than above. The artificial lighting was dim yet even, a pale version of evening in the city above—it seemed, somehow, easier for those final thousands from the city's outskirts to make the downward metamorphosis at night.

Along the broad underground tunnels, more like avenues, the later arrivals streamed. People's Liberation Army cadre directed families to intervening ration stations. Public toilets and dispensaries were clearly marked. Bedding for those with none was piled high on movable platforms. To the left and right were cross-tunnels leading to other main arteries. PLA cadre on motorized scooters and bicycles crisscrossed through the orderly mass. Many of those new denizens of the world below knew that several years before an underground railway had been built in Beijing running across the city from east to west. Later on other lines appeared.

The underground was a transport artery. The tunnels ran on two levels—at a depth of twenty-five and fifty feet. They could accommodate four million people, about half the population in the main section of the city. Tunnels on the first level were about seven feet high and four feet wide, vaulted with concrete ceilings. The main tunnels, which were broad enough for traffic, were on the second, deeper level. The tunnels could withstand anything short of a direct nuclear hit, the people had been told, and a system of air filters provided protection from radiation.

The Chinese people had built a "modern underground Great Wall."

People began to talk once more, as if they had died and traveled to the old Middle Kingdom at the center of the earth to be reunited with their countless ancestors. A baby wailed. A distant rumble from the parallel avenues sounded steadily. The loudspeakers lining the arteries crackled above the low calls and the steady hum of talk.

Aboveground, from the Gates of Heaven to the Forbidden City, the lights went out. China went dark.

Suddenly, below, the multitude stopped. The loudspeakers blared out the opening strains of "The East Is Red." Then the volume was lowered, a pause, no one moved. A voice broke the electronic and human silence—

"COMRADE HU WILL SPEAK . . ."

"COMRADES. MEN AND WOMEN OF THE PEOPLE'S REPUBLIC OF CHINA. THE WORLD WILL REMARK AND HISTORY WILL NEVER FORGET THE HEROIC, COOR-DINATED EFFORT TODAY IN BEIJING CITY AND ACROSS CHINA. A MASS MOVEMENT OF AN ENTIRE POPULATION UNEQUALED IN THE ANNALS OF TIME. I SALUTE YOU.

"THIS IS THE SITUATION THAT CHINA FACES TO-NIGHT. MOSLEM AND TURKISH POPULATIONS IN THE FAR WEST HAVE ELECTED TO CROSS OVER INTO THE CONTIGUOUS REPUBLICS OF THE SOVIET UNION. THERE OUR HEROIC NATIONAL MINORITIES WILL JOIN INSURGENT UZBEKS AND KAZAKS IN THE STRUGGLE FOR AUTONOMY OF THEIR BROTHERS FROM SOVIET TYRANNY.

"THE UNITED STATES OF AMERICA WILL TOMOR-

ROW DELIVER TO THE USURPERS IN THE SOVIET UNION CERTAIN COMMUNICATIONS CONCERNING THE SECURITY OF THE PEOPLE'S REPUBLIC OF CHINA. SHOULD THE SOCIAL IMPERIALISTS OF RUSSIA OPPOSE US, THEN WE, THE PEOPLE OF CHINA, ARE PREPARED TO STRUGGLE FOR GENERATIONS UNTIL VICTORY. WE ARE PREPARED FOR A PEOPLE'S WAR. WE HAVE FULFILLED THE DICTUM OF CHAIRMAN MAO, 'DIG TUNNELS DEEP, STORE GRAIN EVERYWHERE!'

"YES, COMRADES, WE ARE PREPARED TO WAIT, TO 'SIT ON THE MOUNTAIN AND LOOK ON WHILE THE TIGERS FIGHT.' WE ARE INDEED WELL PLACED, BECAUSE EUROPE, AS WELL, WILL FIGHT AGAINST THE SOVIET UNION TO THE LAST MAN. AND WE, THE CHINESE PEOPLE, SHALL WATCH AND WAIT, AND WE SAY AGAIN IN A VOICE HEARD ROUND THE WORLD— *'WHEN THE HOUR COMES, WE SHALL FLAY YOU, DRAW YOUR SINEWS, AND SCATTER THE ASHES TO THE WINDS.'*

" 'WHEN WILL THE HOUR ARRIVE?' YOU ASK. DO YOU NOT REMEMBER CHAIRMAN MAO'S STORY OF THE WISE MAN AND THE FOOL?—

"A FOOLISH OLD MAN WENT TO NORTH MOUNTAIN AND BEGAN TO DIG; A WISE OLD MAN PASSED BY AND SAID, 'WHY DO YOU DIG, YOU FOOLISH OLD MAN? DO YOU NOT KNOW THAT YOU CANNOT MOVE THE MOUNTAIN WITH A LITTLE SHOVEL?' BUT THE FOOLISH OLD MAN ANSWERED, 'WHILE THE MOUNTAIN CANNOT GET ANY HIGHER, IT WILL GET LOWER WITH EACH SHOVELFUL. WHEN I PASS ON, MY SONS AND HIS SONS, AND HIS SONS' SONS WILL GO ON MAKING THE MOUNTAIN LOWER. WHY CAN'T WE MOVE THE MOUNTAIN?' AND THE FOOLISH OLD MAN KEPT DIGGING,

AND THE GENERATIONS THAT FOLLOWED AFTER
HIM, AND THE WISE OLD MAN LOOKED ON IN DIS-
GUST. BUT THE RESOLUTENESS AND THE SPIRIT OF
THE GENERATIONS THAT FOLLOWED THE FOOLISH
OLD MAN TOUCHED GOD'S HEART, AND GOD SENT
TWO ANGELS WHO PUT THE MOUNTAIN ON THEIR
BACKS AND MOVED IT.

"THIS IS THE STORY MAO TOLD. WHEN HE SPOKE OF
GOD HE MEANT THE SIX HUNDRED MILLION WHO
HAD HELPED HIM TO MOVE THE OLD OPPOSITION,
THE GREAT MOUNTAINS. . . ."

Mr. Hu sat back and sighed. He lit his first cigarette since descending into the netherworld. He closed his eyes, ignored the tea
the orderly had put before him on the broadcasting console. In his
mind he could see the empty streets above; on his table he saw the
empty message clipboard—no further word from Manheim had
come. China in its millions had departed from the face of the earth
and Mr. Hu could see them all scattered across the breadth of the
country under the earth, the people in their vastness, in the shadows, in the tunnels, on the two subterranean levels. As the orderly
watched, Mr. Hu's head nodded and jerked up, then nodded
again . . .

The orderly removed the burning cigarette stub from Mr. Hu's
nicotine-stained fingers, and stared in terror at his own reflection
in the glass walls of the Vice-Chairman's broadcasting booth.

20

WASHINGTON, D.C.—JANUARY 27, 1984
(FRIDAY)

It was twenty minutes past eight in the morning when her doorbell rang at the Watergate. When she saw who it was she opened up the blanket that she had wrapped herself in and took him in against her warm naked body and held him—her love for him mingling with pity at the sight of his gaunt and haunted face. "What happened? What have they done to you?"

"I needed you. Let's get down to the 'safe suite,' the media are about fifteen minutes behind us. I have an aide setting up a diversion that might help a little; the streets are all blocked off by the police. Go ahead, I don't have to leave for Camp David until tonight."

She took a step backward and rubbed at a red spot beneath her left breast where a button from his raincoat had marked her. She watched as an ember began to rise in his hollow eyes. She felt her nipples going hard and a warm mottling across her breasts. His hands trembled as he reached out for her and it was as if from a great height that he knelt on his haunches in front of her. Kneeling, his open ivory colored raincoat played out around him like a robe.

In the antiseptic safe suite they finally settled for tea and melted cheese on English muffins. He barely ate his because, he said, there was less chance of a crippling headache, at a time like this, if he fasted.

"Are they worse?" she asked.

"No. Better. Until this situation . . . Andy told me what he did. You saw Arbatov?"

"Yes. What happened in California?

"The Secret Service estimate is that two million people may be in Washington within thirty-six hours. They're calling it a 'prerevolutionary situation' . . . If they knew what's really happening they'd be heading in the other direction. You talked to Arbatov?"

"Wolf, I asked what happened in California? What happened to Andy Kott?"

"Andy? What do you mean?"

"He called me. He said that Wick—"

"I left early, without notice, with just the SS because Wick and Kott were not on the grounds—I was told. What did Kott tell you?"

"Well . . . He was hysterical—but he made sense. He said that Wick tried to kill him—"

"No."

"And that I should go to Virginia and get his family evacuated because the bombs were coming."

"Now I understand why the SS told me that what actually happened was that Andy had some sort of breakdown—after a very tense, very long meeting before dinner—and ran into the woods and Peter Wick ran after him . . ."

"What time was this?"

"I was told this took place about ten o'clock."

"California time?"

"That's right."

"And he said—"

"That Peter Wick was trying to kill him, and that Wick meant wolf in Polish and that you should watch out and that the Order of Battle—"

"The Order of Battle? *On your phone?* He's out of his goddamned mind—you didn't call his wife, did you?"

"No. I went out to see her."

"No."

"Yes, Wolf, I did. He sounded crazy with fear—and I think he was injured somehow—but not *crazy* crazy."

"What did you tell Molly?"

"What he asked me to. To take the little girl and get out. I was very impressed with Molly. I'm very impressed with both Andy and Molly. The child is kind of sad, their life can't be very easy, can it? She was terribly concerned about you."

"Me?"

"Yes. Me too . . . Wolf, did they set up that meeting in California so that if you rejected their plan, whatever it was, they could . . . keep you there?"

"I don't know."

"Wolf, I believe Andy Kott. He is a decent and, I think, a very brave young man . . ."

He sat hunched over the tea as if warming himself. She walked around behind him and massaged the cords of muscles around his neck and shoulders. "A hot bath," she said. He gazed up at her again. She undressed him, dropping the clothes on the floor as they crossed to the bathroom. He leaned on the sink as she ran the water, drooping his head with his weight on one foot.

"I did see Georgi Arbatov—thank you for trusting me and for letting me help." He let this go by. "I know him, as you know, and I think that he may be your best hope in this thing. Arbatov believes that the so-called four conditions—Cuba, Cambodia, et cetera—would be an insupportable humiliation to the USSR, that the Politburo would never accept—but you knew that. I think his hope is that negotiations between you and him can be tricked up to assure each side of progress, and stretched out until popular protests force some concessions."

"Meaning?"

"Well, I mean your talks start as of tomorrow, don't they? Here, get in. It's hot. You have to relax, sleep before you go up to the hawk's nest at Camp David. I'm exhausted, too. First Andy called, then the bloody helicopters started circling in droves about five o'clock this morning. And I was missing you, and scared."

He sank down in the tub as far as he could and closed his eyes and as she soaped him Wolf told her about Bohemian Grove. She undressed and began to wash herself with a cloth, thoroughly and quickly, the way women who travel a good deal do. They dried each other and went to lie naked on the bed.

He told her about Winston and the brass, their emptiness, their death wish, and hinted at the demands that had been added to his already unacceptable list. "They gave me a loaded gun to take in to Arbatov and put to his head. Together with what they knew somehow that Hu had laid on me, it was a double-barreled gun. I have very little time to decide what to do."

She traced the definition of his neck and shoulders and rubbed her long flank against him. "Wolf, you said that the Chinese see the Japanese militarists of the '30s and '40s when they look at the Soviet Union, and Georgi Arbatov told me last night, or rather two nights ago, that when the Russians look at China they see a potential giant version of Germany in World War II. But what is it that has terrified the United States so much that she has become like the PRC and the USSR, sharing that same vision of entrapment? The United States has never been butchered and enslaved by a world war. It makes no sense. I've been racking my brain, trying to understand all over again why this is happening . . . ah, I love you, my lover . . ." She drew his hand over and locked it between her legs.

"*They're* still terrified of Japan and Germany respectively. America? We live in the shadows of our own bombs. . . . I don't think you understood what I said before . . . I'm being forced to take a much harsher, *much harsher,* list of demands in to Arbatov, harsher even than Hu wanted me to go in with."

She sat up abruptly but before she could cry out he reached up and gripped her shoulder with his long fingers. ". . . Wait, listen, this is what I want to tell you—I love you, B.J., I need you and I want to take you away and have a child with you—"

She went rigid under his hands. Then, slowly, she settled on his chest with her lips at his ear, so that they clung to each other, clasped in each other's arms, murmuring sounds, half-words.

She thinking and partly saying . . . so long, searching so long for the one man . . . my father, the father of my child . . . searching for men on white horses, all vanity, wanting to have them, devour them, swallow them, birth them, *be* them . . . like my mother, my grandmother, yet *not* like them . . .

All the words were melded together into moans when he began to suck her breasts. "My baby," she said out loud. He looked up at her. "Dawson Island," he whispered. "We go by forced marches. First to Dawson Island in the Strait of Magellan, then depending on whether there is all-out war or not we could go from there to—"

A helicopter chopped into hearing and then away again. As she looked at him her eyes slowly gathered into focus. "I don't understand, Wolf."

"I'm not going to see the President or talk to Arbatov. And I'm not going to flash Hu his green-light signal—from what Winston said I can see that it won't stop Hu anyway. Andy was right. They are killers . . . B.J., Dawson is in the Antarctic, at Tierra del Fuego.

I have the coded plans for the U.S. installation there as part of my security brief."

"What are you talking about, Wolf?" The two of them were sitting up now in bed.

"I'm sorry, listen . . . our people are commited to a plan over the next sixty days that involves subversion within the Soviet Union and a *casus belli* in the Persian Gulf that leads to a tactical nuclear strike by us. They want to use me, like the Japanese in Washington at the time of Pearl Harbor used their ambassador to cover for their plans, by holding talks with Arbatov, who, by the way, they also plan to eliminate. There's no ultimatum now instead of a war—it's to be an ultimatum in preparation for one, although I didn't know that when I came back from Beijing and pitched the pros and cons of the China Card to the President. Betsy, we leave now or not at all. There'll be a state of National Emergency declared within forty-eight hours, timed to coincide with the President's U.N. speech and the start of the so-called Manheim-Arbatov talks—"

"Andy was *not* crazy."

"No. We won't be able to move. The entire National Security Council will be moved into the special Pentagon underground shelters—the same will happen in Beijing and Moscow—and the meetings with Arbatov would be conducted somewhere underground, surrounded by armed men. Jarrell and the SS would become my jailers, that much I know. You, despite who you are, and despite being British, would be detained and held incommunicado. We'd probably never see each other again."

She stood up to stare down at him, feeling for something to wrap around her nakedness.

"Wolf, I want you and a baby and a world to *live* in. What are you *saying?* . . ." They were still talking only one notch above whispers and had to pause as the sound of helicopters stuttered in and out. "We can't have it both ways. Either you convince the President that his military is out of control and to let you talk to

Arbatov from a survival position, or you threaten to go public *right
now* (as she had asked Arbatov to do)—we'll start with Washington
and London—and that would make it very hard to impose martial
law on this country . . . Wolf, what choice is there? *You* of all people
imagining that we can somehow play Adam and Eve in the icy
wastes of—where, what island did you—?"

"Dawson. You know, where the CIA and the junta set up camps
after the coup in Chile—"

"*Chile?* Wolf, you killed that boy in this room and I helped you,
and you swore to me that—"

"I did *not* lie to you. I was not *part* of it. But I'm telling you that
with the help of some people I know we can get out of here today
and that if we wait we're finished. The people, believe me, are not
going to save us—not in China, not in Russia, and not here. I
drafted a second signal to Hu—saying that the situation here was
getting out of hand—and I stood over Wick and his warrant officer
and made them transmit it. The antiwar movement may be huge
but it's unarmed. It lives and talks the First Amendment; it can't
go to guerrilla warfare in one night."

His voice died away. His chest was heaving now. Each watching
the other could see the beginning signs of shock.

She felt as if he had hit her in the mouth with his fist. "Wolf
. . . Georgi Arbatov knows your position. He understands that it
will take time, a few weeks, to raise popular demonstrations . . .
He's prepared to stall, I'm certain. We mustn't panic. The President
—"

"The President has lost control." His voice was low, unsteady
now. "He knows that they'll kill him if they have to, like
they—"

"Wolf, with the hunger strike spreading across the country, if
you go public like you did after Cambodia—"

"But that was different. There was time then. Listen, the official
shelters here are over twenty years old. You wouldn't believe it—

people used to screen films down in what's called the Executive Situation Room—the shelters have about as much utility as an airport lounge. The people on the 'Blue Team'—that's the designation for the thousand or so top government elite—would be at each other's throats after the first day. They ran a test in '82 and half of the chemical toilets were no longer functional. The congressmen and their wives and their mistresses and their aides all go out to a mountain shelter in Virginia, where there are provisions for no more than *eight days.* It's a damn *Führerbunker,* a while-you-wait concrete tomb . . . For the rest of the population—even if there was a cessation of hostilities after the first exchange—this would be a nation of barbed wire, a patchwork of battlefields. I know. I helped draw up the plan for SAD, the Special Analysis Division of the Office of Emergency Preparedness. In D.C., *you* could end up in the first roundup of the 'ENAL'—enemy alien list. And forget about going back to England. We have joint contingency plans. Both countries will be divided up into autonomous regions with 'Regional Seats of Government' buried underground. Each region under absolute military control, no contact with London or Washington."

Her shoulders were numb where he continued to grip. His chest heaved. Her voice shook. " 'It's a *boy!' That's* what Teller wired the brass after the first successful H-bomb test. 'It's a *boy!'*

" 'SAD' and 'MAD'—and the code names for the first bombs over Japan were 'Little *Boy'* and 'Big *Man'* . . . Ah, you men. You've blunted the English language and now you want to kill us with it. Get up now, Wolf, stand up, speak on that telephone to London and—"

"Betsy, you think from what Andy Kott told you that he understood the entire Order of Battle? The poor bastard. Under Cheyenne Mountain, deep down, at this minute the watch officers of the North American Aerospace Defense Command are sitting at Red Alert waiting for the beeping sound to start up from the computer terminal. Strategic Air Command B-52s have been scrambling now for the last twenty-four hours. The missile teams manning the ICBMs are on Red Alert. In Hawaii the order goes out to the Pacific Fleet. The lines are being held open for the conference call that will take place among the generals at NORAD, SAC, and the National Military Command Post. But I won't initiate that call. Peter Wick could, though, and he could give the correct authentication and say, 'Gentlemen, the President has asked me to communicate to you his complete faith in your decision-making process.'

"And do you know what the process is, Betsy? A forty-six-cent chip the size of a dime will 'tell' the Wimex, the Worldwide Military Command and Control System, will tell the bloody Wimex that it's *time.*"

"All right, Wolf, I'm sure that Andy Kott did not know a fraction of what you know—"

He wanted to tell her that he *had* tried to reason with the President before the China trip. . . .

He had had to pull rank even to talk to the Chief Executive alone at Camp David. Only Andy Kott knew that he had shuttled up to the snowbound camp on the NSC helicopter. For security, Wolf and the President had begun a half-mile trudge through the snow, talking in low voices, staying well away from the perimeter of Secret Service men in their quilted cold weather jackets and bright earmuffs.

The President's steps were short and shuffling on the frozen path, his face an unhealthy hue. He had aged frighteningly in the last years and his short span of concentration, Wolf knew, would tolerate only one brief plea. Already the chief was turning back toward the polished log lodge, bent against the wind. Only minutes left to persuade this man who—if he did not trust him—did respect him and had once listened to him.

"Mr. President, I know that during my mission to China the DOD and the joint chiefs and Winston are going to urge you to begin a preparatory gearing up of the antisatellite arsenal—careful, sir, that's very slippery—"

"Wolf, let's walk back, I can't take the cold anymore . . . the ASAT? Oh, yes. General Kramer tells me that the Air Force's Tank-Car, what's it called? . . ."

"The Big Bird."

"Yes, that's it. That the Big Bird has a smaller, new satellite, a . . . what do they—?"

"The ferret."

"This ferret thing can monitor the Soviet's field telephones. They're heat-sensing and . . . and they can monitor and, uh, take out the Russian ASAT system and all their spacecraft—"

"One moment sir, that is what I'm trying to clarify. The Soviet space city at Plesetsk could detect any overt anticipatory maneuver such as that on our part and take irreversible action . . ."

The President shuffled to a halt and hugged his overcoat in a closer embrace. Wolf, towering over him, looked down on the diminished figure in the corduroy hunting cap. The man's ears were a bloodless white in the freezing wind. Wolf beat his arms for warmth.

"Wait," the President said.

The Secret Service men had jogged ahead to the headquarters lodge to signal that the President would be entering momentarily. The mid-morning sun was almost totally obscured now by the snow clouds driving out of the northeast. "Wait," he mumbled, "what do you mean 'irreversible' action?" The cold had numbed the President's purpled lips so that Wolf had to almost stoop to decipher the question.

"Sir, the consequences could be terrible. The Soviet X-20A, their 'Dyna-Soar' or Dynamic Soaring Glider—their space shuttle—has always been capable of supplying, at five times the speed of sound, their Salyut spaceships—"

"Dinosaur," the Chief stuttered through chattering teeth and tried to step toward the waiting lodge. In frustration Wolf took the President's arm as if to help him over the frozen flagstones and managed to hold him stationary a moment longer.

"Yes, sir. Both sides now depend almost exclusively on their satellites for communications and surveillance. The loser in a space shoot-out will be the one who's not able to tell what's going on at the enemy's ICBM sites on earth. If that happened, a preemptive nuclear strike might well seem obligatory to our joint chiefs or theirs . . . Sir, if we radically redeploy our space assets at this time, the Soviets will certainly interpret that move as aggressive."

The Chief looked up. The wind had brought fluid to his eyes— or, Wolf decided, he *could* be crying. The near-sighted eyes gazed through cold tears and the driving clouds in the direction of the mountains, unseeing. "I'm told . . . they told me . . . that unmanned satellites in outer space, firing lasers, would not involve personnel or civilians, only . . . you know, hardware. Skylab and—"

"Salyuts."

". . . that the worst that could happen would be a . . . a computer war."

"No, sir. They told you wrong."

"They told me wrong?

"Yes, sir."

A bent-over woman in a ranch mink coat reaching almost to the icy ground came stepping out of the lodge, leaning on the arm of a shivering Secret Service agent. She waved a gloved hand. "Hot chocolate," she called out.

"Coming, honey," the Commander in Chief mumbled after a moment. The tears or whatever, made their slow, cold progress down his cheeks. He leaned on the arm of his National Security Adviser and curled his lips back in an act of willpower, in a forlorn attempt to flash a smile at his wife. . . .

Wolf found himself unable to go on to tell Betsy that the President had become, under the tension of the protracted crisis, a hollow man who could not act; that the restless, seeking figure that she remembered from the campaigns was no more. Only a few advisers knew it, and at a time like this their lips were sealed to protect a President who, though certainly never described to anyone as a giant, had at least, never been perceived as pitiful.

"Betsy, you don't understand. The President acted like . . . well, I don't see what *I* could say—"

He tried to tell her about the "holocaust drills" on the Washington Mall that had aborted. About the cabinet officers, arriving in limousines, running toward the helicopters; how the long limousines would get snarled up, the choppers breaking down under the maximum weight. Telling her about Mt. Weather in the Blue Ridge Mountains of Virginia (where the Kott family would have been directed to report) dug out to house construction workers and their bulldozers: laborers who would have to help dig them out after the attack. All of these men—workers and officials—were termed "non-interruptibles."

"What's happened to us?" she said. The moon caught her hair and part of her anguished profile. "What's happened to the awe we used to feel seeing nuclear explosions made by cameras on atolls in the Pacific? The horror after Nagasaki . . . the tension of the '50s . . . what's happened to us, Wolf? Are we already dead? . . . You know still more that you're not telling me, don't you? That extremists in your country gave classified weapons to China. The China Card . . . Yes, I know about that. That war-hawks have been trying since Dallas, since the Gulf of Tonkin, to plunge their country into a war with the Soviet Union—"

"Betsy—I can't get on television to say that! They'll have me in a straitjacket in St. Elizabeth's—they'll have you—If we want to live we—"

"Live? God, yes, Wolf, I want to live—to *live* with you and have our baby. But we can't exist outside of the human race. Either everybody lives or nobody—you know that."

"That's not true, Betsy. Even in all-out war, firestorms and all, the estimates say that between five and ten million people will survive. But I agree with you—*we,* you and I, can't survive like moles underground with a handful of self-deluded cowards. If we get out now, at least we have a chance . . . Betsy, I've had it, I just want . . ." His voice ran out.

She walked around the bed slowly. "My darling," she said without touching him. And then, "Georgi Arbatov swears that within five days there will be uprisings from Novocherkassk right across the Soviet Union. My God, why won't you listen? What are you staring at? Wolf—it won't work—the Germans tried to play the American Card against the Soviets and that didn't work, and neither will playing the China—Wolf, *what are you staring at?* Wolf, look at me, you love me. Yes, you love me, but I will die. Think of all the people, keep your mind on *all the bodies . . .*"

He reached out toward her. "Listen," he said, looking away, up and toward the helicopter. "Listen, don't tell me about survival. I know how to survive. Do you know *anything?* Do you know how we survived in Buchenwald. By never for one second allowing ourselves to feel pity for those who were already doomed. No grand design. We're animals, flesh and blood, and we survive as ourselves, not as some racial ideal. I'm not Bertrand Russell and you're not Joan of Arc . . . *Life has no purpose beyond itself*—that's the lesson of the death camps—"

"That's not true, Wolf. Others survived. Your father—"

"Don't mention my father. My father was a Communist—you might as well know—my father was a *hero."*

"No—Wolf—your father was a Nazi—"

His spine arched up and his head shot back, eyes rolling. She lunged to hold him—"I mean he was an officer, a German off—" But she had miscalculated. It was too late. His skin turned pure white before her eyes, and then he pitched headlong at her feet.

21

BUCHENWALD—AUGUST 23, 1944

The tallow candle smoked and smelled bad to the boy. Since the August darkness had fallen, some time after seven, Doctors Rath and Kraft had been trying to contact a spirit who had passed beyond the world of the death camps. The orderlies Peiper and Stein had been invited in, and the boy had sneaked in after the lights had been turned out.

"Father Thyle, can you tell us what is coming?" Dr. Kraft was a cadaverous, mournful-looking man who in real life had been an assistant coroner in Silesia. Now, in the near dark, he asked the ghost of the little monk to provide guidance about the events that they all knew were at hand.

The strange behavior of the scientific inmates was a response to a carefully guarded underground secret: on the next day, August 24, Allied bombers would attack Buchenwald. Those in the know were electrified with hope, and fear. Several of the orderlies who were usually the most realistic, not to say cynical, of men had run to a window to point up at a particularly bright star and one of them, Peiper, had actually croaked in his rough voice—"It is written in the holy books that at the end of the massacre the Lord will kindle the star of peace in heaven." Well, it was to be a kind of deliverance, a second coming . . .

How much did the Germans know? An order was to be issued by the SS, according to the underground rumors, for the destruction of all Jewish and Gypsy children in the camp, but at the same time certain of the guards were beginning to display signs of worry and a desire to curry favor with leaders of the underground. The hospital, meanwhile, was bulging with political prisoners taken out of the death arrivals pouring in from the East. Besides the politicals that the underground was hiding in the hospital, there remained a fraction of actual patients who were dying from typhus in the summer heat and stench. So that was how it happened that the boy was crouched in the airless wardroom while a pale-faced Dr. Kraft pled for information from beyond the known.

The boy was about to crawl out and look for his father, who had not been seen since early morning, when Dr. Kraft rose and in a whisper began to speak in a voice uncannily like that of Father Thyle. His eyes were wide, his lower lip drooped . . . "The SS will order roll call but the prisoners will not respond, they will break ranks, *for the first time.* And a Jew will cry out in a terrible voice *'mene, mene, tekel, parsin'*—'you have been weighed and found wanting.' The camp police will scream and threaten . . ."

At that moment a hand reached in and dragged the boy by the belt of his trousers out of the door and into the corridor.

"*Shh!* Follow me." The boy bobbed along behind the broad back of Dr. Manheim until they reached Room 42. Room 42, sweltering and reeking of carbolic acid, had, until just before the boy's arrival at the camp, been used as a holding cell for the SS scientific "experimentations," but since January these experiments had stopped; perhaps in anticipation of a future judgment. Or perhaps, as the French orderly said, it was only because their subjects always died and the SS orderlies had nightmares afterward. Most probably the worst of the torture was ended because Dr. Manheim had let Dr. Ding-Schuyler know that evidence of the atrocities was already secreted in Weimar against the day of Germany's defeat. Dr. Manheim would do his best, he promised, to see that the Americans and not the Russians got their hands on the damning documents. He knew that the Nazis feared the Russians above any other threat in the world. The boy smelled the familiar odors as the doctor pushed the door shut behind him, sat down and mopped his face. The fat harvest moon looked through the barred window and bathed the retort cases and shiny laboratory instruments in blue light. "The whole camp is going mad," sighed the doctor, "they all know something's up. It was everything I could do to keep our own people from premature action. I have to go out again but I want to talk to you first—tomorrow anything could happen . . . Come, Wolfie, sit down here.

"According to Ding-Schuyler, Himmler is leaving response to any Allied attack to the 'discretion' of the Camp Commandant. In other words, when the planes drop their bombs tomorrow, what will the Commandant do? There are now some forty-seven thousand men crammed into this camp, and one misstep could panic Koch and Pfister into a bloodbath . . ."

The father hurried on telling the boy what to do if this or that contingency suddenly presented itself. If anything should happen to him, the doctor stressed, then the boy would have to go into the underground. At last the full meaning of that term "underground" was spelled out for him by the big man with the bulging eyes. The shadows that the boy had seen at night scurrying from barrack to barrack were underground agents and couriers working to effect a compromise with the non-Communist resistance in the camp led by British officers. Bargains had been struck and alternate plans agreed on. An impressive arms cache was now to be shared by both insurgent groups. Between them a "comrades court" had been set up to pass sentence on and deal with unreconstructed kapos and the last of the camp double-agents. News from the BBC was actually being piped through the barracks loudspeaker system at night in place of the military marches and Nazi propaganda that were played all during the day. The boy would have to stand his share of guard duty at night in order to sound a warning if for some reason the SS decided to come into the camp, the doctor instructed. And, again, after tomorrow anything could happen including, he said, his own disappearance, but that the boy should not be so frightened. He reached out and put his wide, square hand on the boy's shoulder, then stroked his cheek.

They sat there in the shadow, streaked by the moon's light, without talking, the boy shivering in spite of the heat. The doctor lifted his left hand and turned on the overhead light. "Come, Wolfie." He led the boy over to the table where the microscopes stood.

"Let others tell fortunes and hold séances, let the whole camp run amok, but you use this, you use your head and never lose sight of the goal. Here, look into this, do you see the culture on the slide?" The boy pressed his eye to the eyepiece of the microscope and saw on the strip of glass below a teeming constellation of bacteria.

"Wolfie, that is *life*—keep looking. Life is *life,* not a belief in the gods, or in the ghost of Father Thyle, or even in the Allies—life is an activity. You must survive—I'm saying it again—in order to tell the world of what *has* happened and what *will* happen, unless . . . Your body is made up of billions of living cells like those on the slide . . . as old as time itself. You are the first man and the last man. We all are. And all that protoplasm has a tendency, a talent. *You* have a *talent,* an instinct, a *tendency* to live—built right into your biology . . ." The boy heard in his father's voice a new anxiety, of special deliberate emphasis, as though the doctor was, for once, unsure of what he said—as though Wolf's believing would have to be for both of them. He kept his eye to the microscope as his father started again. "You know, in your body, all the way down to the invisible parts of your blood and bones, there is an inheritance, not merely from your father, but from before we were men, before we were even mammals—you know what mammals are? I'm talking about before a million years ago, I'm saying fifty, a hundred million, a *billion*. Yes. What you're watching on the slide is billions of years old in its form and its behavior."

The boy looked up. The big man was dripping wet from the heat and tension, his cotton shirt and trousers were soaked through. The doctor turned out the light again. The boy felt the indentation that the microscope had made on the sweaty skin around his eye. The doctor moved away from the grid of moonbeams to talk more about a talent for life.

"So there are millions of years of survival packed away inside you, Wolfie. You're very frightened now, and when the bombs land tomorrow—we will have only a few minutes warning, but you will be safe with Peyser, he knows where to hide, he'll never leave your side—but fear is the key to life. Too much of it and you're paralyzed, too little and they pick you off—but the right amount mobilizes you to function—like those cells on the slide, it sets up the warning system—that's what your nervous system is, when all's said and done, a warning system. You have it inside you and the inmates in the camp have it and all of mankind has it."

The big man flicked a spray of water, sweat and tears, from his face. "Even the SS has it. You've seen the look on their faces the last few days. Whatever happens, stick with Peyser and the hospital comrades—and remember who you are, Wolfie. Remember your dear *mutti* . . . she tried her best, she believed in science, in truth, she loved you very much. It was I who insisted that to save herself she should marry Colonel Hoder. And he is not a bad man, just weak. It is the times that killed her, like so many . . . *ja,* you will do what you have to do to survive. A new world is coming, Wolfie, and the old world—the one we knew and loved without questioning it—is going down. So now we question everything, we make a new world, we make our natural fear work *for* us—that's all. The old world, everything we held sacred, is gone. From now on we live for and among our fellow men and we remind ourselves and them that we are men, and the instant that we see other men acting as if they were gods, as if they were more than mere men, as if they could not die—then we warn them that they, too, can die. And then, if they refuse to pay attention to our warning, we *show them* that they can die. That is the warning that you are going to take out of here," he said, smashing his huge hand down on the tray table, making everything jump.

When the doctor stood he blocked out the weak moonlight entirely. There was a premonitory quiet in the ward outside. "Listen, Wolfie, don't give up, whatever happens." (Ironically, it was perhaps easier to say and do at that terrible time than forty years later —at a far more threatening time.)

The boy felt himself swept up in the iron clasp of the powerful, sweaty arms. He had understood some of it, including the part about not being God, and dying, and the cells in bacteria and how human beings had the same old cells. And he understood, too well, the last words of the fierce man that he loved—Good-bye, my son."

The next morning the bombers did not come. The boy knew that the doctor was dead or at least arrested when the SS poured across the camp grounds at dawn. The guard dogs bit at random, the din was terrible, there was the steady tattoo of machine guns and pistols —the camp seemed to have gone completely berserk at last. Then, suddenly, the children were being herded together in the parade area. Peyser went down under a rifle bullet, Rath was shot where he stood, screaming at the SS that "Herr Dr. Ding-Schuyler will hear of this—"

The boys, most of them under twelve, called out for fathers or protectors. The dogs tore at them while the guards pulled and kicked in a fear-inspired rage. Within twenty minutes a wall of carbines surrounded the boys on three sides, crowding them against a wire fence. From the barracks came wails from those who had believed that they would never, *could* never, ever again, feel such loss—they who had lost, they thought, the capacity for pity and grief.

Criminals and Communists, Gypsies and Jews, kapos and informers screamed out loud inside the tomb of their bodies as the guards opened fire. And as they did the bomber planes broke through the sound. The boys lay where they had been shot and the SS ran from the falling bombs, tripping over dogs, rolling on the ground.

Wolfgang had dropped, unconscious, at the first fusillade. He lay frozen as death, as if he had been a plant on the bottom of a lake whose surface was covered with an impenetrable layer of ice. He never heard the guards coming, or even the shooting, or the planes either, because he was in a cataleptic seizure.

As soon as the raid had passed, a hospital kapo, Koening, began to shout at a work gang to drag the bodies of the dead boys to the ditch behind the riding hall, just north of the hospital.

The boy's body was absolutely rigid, flying through the air with the rest. He never felt the earth-covering hastily thrown in over them by the terrified work gang.

Fourteen hours passed and the boy still floated, frozen where he had been flung, among the bodies, suspended in a sea of cold flesh.

Not until long after dark was he able to move so much as a finger. Only a light covering of dirt had been thrown in on the bodies, and barrels of oil left at the rim of the pit; tomorrow they would be disposed of completely. When he opened his eyes the boy could see nothing, nor could he move, though half of him stuck up out of the dirt. So he lay there with the soil of death in his mouth. He could not remember anything. He *believed* that he was dead. But, as ordered, he had survived.

22

WASHINGTON, D.C.—JANUARY 28, 1984
(SATURDAY)

She lay, clothed again, with her head at the foot of the narrow bed. Below her, on the floor, he was stretched out where he had pitched and fallen some eleven hours earlier. The dusky gloom was severed every few minutes by the helicopter beam that circled in and out at the far perimeter of the complex.

His naked body had lain arched, as though frozen, the muscles tensed, until she covered him with the bedspread and got herself dressed. Her electric watch said 8:11 and she lay back to compute the time in London. Editorial had stood by since the crisis had begun. It was time to—

She heard him muttering dimly, names that sounded German, but the low guttural reflex sounds yielded no meaning that she could make out. It was time. With her left hand she felt for the Luger at her side. She rested the fingertips of her left hand on the cold barrel. With the fingers of her right hand she felt in the dark

269

for his bulk under the spread, but her reach fell short of where he lay stretched on the floor.

After a minute she picked up the Luger and looked down into the muzzle. A black hole in the twilight, the inside of the barrel drawing her deeper into its oily-smelling darkness. "Is that what it smells like?" she thought, and then the dread hit her. She could face someone's dying; had faced it with B.R., with her mother. But death, Death—that was different.

She closed her eyes trying to hold onto B.R.'s face as it had looked toward the end. "I should so like to live," she could hear him say, and then the ancient visage began to fade. The planes and hollows, reflecting almost a century of struggle melted away from her. She was, she had to admit at last, alone. . . .

The scream that had broken from Wolf as he fell . . . she would never forget it. It was a sound of despair, heartbreaking, as if rising from some spirit of himself, some creature that was trapped by the very body in which it lay, a time-stopping sound, beyond consolation.

She sank deeper, looking for release from the terror that had been pressing on for almost twelve hours now. The dim vistas of the underground city beneath its double, the forbidden one, came up toward her out of memory, and she descended to meet it. . . . In her dream she ran soundlessly, seeking someone. Then she was aware of B.R. Not the patriarch heavy with wisdom and honors that she had served. Rather it was the electric young man of forty, with his fine brow and gray hair, the lean and pointed face atop the stiff high collar, the lithe figure and hungry eyes that turned toward her in the distance. Somehow he was coming at her through the shadows of the Forbidden City, and she could hear the strong timbre of his voice as it must have sounded more than thirty years before her birth, telling her his dream that he had had in China, the time that he had almost died. It was about teaching those who would destroy how "to forget strife, to know the beauty that was their mission to see and embrace . . ." Somehow in the dream she had escaped the Forbidden City and she and a troop of other children ran on the beach at Coln on the coast of Wales, and the sun blazed down holding them all in its easy embrace. Then her mother, Cordy Jones, stuck her head up from under water and floated, looking back at them on the shore, but she was too far away to be heard when she spoke . . . And then the Kott child's asymmetrical face covered the horizon, and the mother, Molly Kott, called out something in a foreign language. The bomb was dropped from a helicopter on the White House. From the State Department to the Pentagon to the National Zoo nothing was left. In Virginia the eyes of the Kotts, mother and daughter, turned to jelly and ran down their cheeks like tears. . . .

The chops from the helicopter blew away the scraps of memory; or had he moved suddenly? "Wolf?" she whispered, using her elbows for leverage. Looking down in the near-darkness she could barely see that his eyes were open. "Wolf." She let go of the gun and leaned over the bed to touch him. He panted shallowly and stared up at her. A pulse in his forehead pumped.

"Don't try to talk or move." She touched his wide, white brow, then pulled the spread up around his bunched shoulders until only his face remained to catch the little light left in the room . . . "It's about 9:00 P.M., you've been out for nearly twelve hours . . . It was serious. I was very worried."

His lips twisted trying to talk but the effort was too much. He was breathing through his mouth in shallow pulls, and his eyes were losing some of their numbness as the pain crowded into them. "My darling, let me talk," she said. "You are so ill. You talked a little in your, ah, state, something about someone named 'Peyser.'

"Wolf, can you understand me? Just nod your head a little. That's it, darling. Now, listen carefully. Wolf, darling, your suffering is over . . . for all of us it's over . . ."

His eyes fixed on her in a look so filled with trust that she began to choke on the words. She pulled the corner of the sheet across her eyes and drove herself on.

"Here's what happened, my love, according to London. I spoke to them twice while you were . . . asleep . . . before the phones went out." She stared through tears deep into the eyes burning in the strangely childlike face. Her throat was constricted so that every word was a swallow of pain, but she spared him, and herself, nothing. She had forced herself to say it, as she'd rehearsed it in her worst fantasy, now come to reality . . .

"At exactly 10:00 A.M. west coast time—today—a twenty-megaton bomb exploded a few hundred feet above street level over the midtown campus of the University of Southern California . . . You know what that means, Wolf. In the first fraction of a second the temperature at ground zero went to a hundred and fifty million degrees Fahrenheit—this is the London *Times* story . . ."

Her speech was labored but clear, to make every word register. The Soviet Union, fearing a first strike by the United States, had itself struck first at Los Angeles with a 200/SS-9 intercontinental ballistic missile. The Russians had struck in order to dictate terms of a Soviet peace, but, she told him, it was too late. The machine of massive retaliation could not be stopped. She knew this ". . . because Jarrell was here with orders to assist you to the Pentagon's underground shelter. The man was wild, I had to threaten him with the Chilean boy's Luger. I think he wanted to kill me. I screamed at him that I'd blow his balls off if he reached for his service revolver . . . then he saw you on the floor. I covered your face and told him that you had been unable to stay on or be a part of a war government. I saw his lips actually tremble and that face finally registered panic, then he said that the Secretary of State and your U.N. ambassador had both taken their own lives. I don't know if it's true, there's no radio or TV or telephone since about three-thirty Washington time . . ."

She was able to speak in a flow now, and still with precision—

speak directly to the look of comprehension rising in his eyes. She could see that he could visualize it happening as she spoke; could see the six-hundred-foot bomb crater, a mile and a half in diameter with a glowing two-hundred-foot-high prominence where the Coliseum had been, and where nothing else was now left above ground level; this smiting of the earth as the unbelievable, burning fireball rebounded toward heaven, expanding, incandescent, reaching proportions of miles in its breadth and height—so bright that aircraft crashed over San Diego, over a hundred miles away, when their pilots were blinded by the flash. She told what she could see him imagining—the freeways, the new skyscrapers, the university set like an alien complex in the center of a black desert, and the people —all evaporated instantly.

Her words were the only intimacy between them now, so she did not hurry or skip. She called him her love, held his gaze, talked of the first minute when the gigantic mushroom rose over southern California just as everyone had always imagined it would. And down below, beneath this cosmic cloud, as the fireball hotter than five thousand suns replaced matter for a radius of five square miles, there was nothing. Beverly Hills, Santa Monica, Ocean Park, to the west; Pasadena, Glendale, Burbank to the east; Inglewood, Hawthorne, Westchester to the south; the Hollywood Hills and canyons to the north: all the network of communities and towns, streets and houses incinerated by the raging thermal wind of the firestorm. Fifteen seconds later the blast wave pulverized anything still standing; a three-hundred-mile-per-hour wind of burning brands roared through tunnels and underground shelters alike to roast those who had thought to try and hide. The heat was so intense that buildings imploded in spontaneous combustion . . . Her hair had fallen around her face as she leaned closer to him, telling it all.

She knew that he could see it. "Those who took shelter underground are all dead." She said it as if it were a reassurance. "The firestorm burned up all the remaining oxygen in the first half hour

. . . it'll be the same in Russia, even in China, for all their secret cities. They'll *all* go," she whispered.

He was trying to say something, he licked his lips. The pulse in his forehead throbbed through the skin. She had to will herself to keep from going down to the floor with him. "There's been no water or any utilities for the last hour," she said, then knelt down beside him and half-kissed, half-quenched him, licking his lips, giving him her saliva. He was parched, on fire. "We can't go down under the ground, we can't go back to the Paleolithic, we can't go back," stroking his forehead like a mother . . .

Ninety miles away, she told him, leaves on trees in Bakersfield burst into flames; downwind of the blast, bushes exploded and the radiation levels rose to five thousand roentgens per hour. Burning clouds raced in all directions, she said, "except it doesn't matter because by now we will have taken out their second tier of cities and they will have wiped out Denver and ours . . . Andy Kott told me that Moscow and Washington would go tomorrow . . . It seems the button-pushers want to give each other time to crawl into the ground and hide."

She was nearly hissing in his ear, gripping his shoulder with rage at the world she was describing. It was time. She crawled to the foot of the bed and tried to reach the pistol. She had to stand up, then come back around and kneel down beside him again.

"My love . . . we are going to die together. I've typed up what we both feel and I want you to sign it."

She held a pen in his long bony hand so that he could sign the statement that had been sticking up out of the typewriter since three o'clock. Then she picked up the gun again and knelt down. His eyes followed her with trust. "I love you, my love," she said over him, her body rocking gently. "We will be together. We will not have our child but we will be more together than either of us ever dreamed . . ."

The tears rolled down her cheeks, dropping onto his hands that lay flat on his chest. "All together," she breathed, "B.R. and my mother and your mother and the people from all the camps . . ." His eyelids fluttered and his right hand on his chest twitched. "Yes," she said, "and not just the innocent either, not just the victims but all the executioners too . . ." The look in his eyes stopped her as if he had called out. She unbuttoned her shirt and pressed her breast to him.

Cradling him, with her right hand she pushed the Luger's safety catch off, biting her lower lip until the taste of blood ran back into her mouth and throat.

His eyes started to wander as the helicopters, three of them now, circled in. She straightened up. She guided his hand onto the cold grip of the Luger, then angled the barrel past his lips and into his mouth.

"I'll follow you," she said, and for a moment, contrary to plan, meant it. His fingers were too stiff to adjust. He might be dying, had been dying for a long time, she knew that now—the pulse beating across his temples could hemorrhage at any time.

A helicopter chopped past, closer this time; her ears were ringing with the mechanical pounding of the rotors as she pulled the trigger.

She recoiled with the shock. She knelt frozen, the Luger motionless in her jerked-up arm. She opened her eyes, the gun caught the light, she watched her own red hand involuntarily turn the barrel toward her, then jerked it away, ordering herself to remember she had a job to do . . . to make the act *mean* something. Otherwise . . .

She was afraid to look down. "B.R., he was dying anyway, was dying since he was a child in the camp, was dying like Andy Kott's poor child. Oh, don't let me give up now. He had to die, And I had to kill him because I love him, love what he believed in too . . . oh God, maybe I'm already carrying his child inside me. I must not give in to guilt. Yes, I have red hands now too—like everybody else.

My days of arrogant innocence were a holiday . . . I want to save life, to create new life . . ."

Her raised gun hand fell. She stood and stumbled toward the illuminated dial of the telephone, grasping in her other hand the blood-flecked page with his signature. The telephone was a security instrument of a kind peculiar to the quarters of the President's staff and a call to London took less than fifteen seconds to put through. She stared, waiting, at the gun and the blood on the table now.

"Tony? B.J. here, put Richard on . . . Richard, put Pamela on the extension and tear out the front page. What? . . . Yes I know you've been standing by all night and no, I bloody well couldn't! . . . Is that you, Pam?—No, I have a heavy cold, I'm . . . not well. All right, stand by, I'm going to dictate it in one take—and, Richard, no copyright on this, I want it to go to the wires simultaneously day and date. Ready?

"Wolfgang H. Manheim (comma) the National Security Adviser to the President of the United States (comma) took his own life tonight in Washington on the eve of negotiations with the Soviet Union (stop) Dr. Manheim had described the meeting as (comma) quotes A last-ditch attempt to avoid nuclear holocaust (stop) Close quotes. (Graph)

"The London *Times* has secured a copy of the high American official's suicide note (stop) Quotes I can no longer act to, in effect, represent a small minority in the government of the United States who intend to use the period of U.S.-USSR negotiations (comma) scheduled to start tomorrow (Sunday) (comma) in order to get into position for hostilities against the Soviet Union (stop) This cannot end otherwise than in mutual nuclear devastation within sixty days (stop) The President has become in effect a prisoner of this small group within the—hold it."

She crossed to the bed and held the gun pointing at the door before the running footsteps had stopped echoing. The door crashed open and Jarrell stood silhouetted in the light from the corridor. He looked from side to side, holding his gun out ahead of him like an antenna, trying to find movement in the darkened room. Behind him she could make out the shadowy figures of Peter Wick and a man she didn't know.

"Mr. Jarrell! I'm a marksman and I'll shoot you if you move." Now he found her silhouette but it was too late. "Mr. Jarrell, Dr. Manheim has taken his life. I found him here. There's an open telephone to London on that table. They can hear every word spoken in this room. Dr. Manheim's death is already on the wires . . . You must leave and inform the White House. I will stay here to finish my statement. Leave *now,* Mr. Jarrell. You too, Mr. Wick."

In the hall, Peter Wick appeared to snap awake, then began to pull Jarrell's partner back and away. Tears were flowing now. As Jarrell backed out, she sidled, feeling for the phone. "Hello Richard? What? I can't . . . I'll tell you about it when I get home. If I get home. What? I have a cold I said—I am *not* crying . . . Richard, don't reach for the end-of-the-world-point heads. You have to split the Manheim suicide with a China story that— . . . No, Richard, wait, goddammit, they're tied together. I want a sidebar—you'll see why—with this quote from Thomas Jefferson—quotes and caps— 'CAN ONE GENERATION BIND ANOTHER AND ALL OTHERS AND THEIR SUCCESSORS FOREVER? I THINK NOT. THE CREATOR MADE THE EARTH FOR THE LIV- ING, AND NOT THE DEAD.' Manheim ended his letter with that from Jefferson's 1781 statement. Please feature that in the suicide letter which will come to you facsimile within the hour by the *Post*'s laser hookup.

"Now, ready? Quotes continue—'The President has become a virtual prisoner of this small group of fanatics in the Joint Chiefs of Staff and the clandestine section of the Central Intelligence

Agency and their agents (stop) (graph).

"The proof of this has been turned over to the *Times* of London for world distribution (stop) 'I was ordered to take part in an act still without a name to describe it, and I could not be a party to it' (stop) (graph) . . ."

CIA GAVE ATOM SECRETS TO CHINA IN THE '50s
DULLES BROTHERS HID
PLAN FROM IKE

BY
BETSY JONES-RUSSELL

On October 16, 1964, at 3:00 P.M. Beijing time, a huge ball of fire seared the autumn sky over Sinkiang, casting a purple sheen on the dusky expanses of the Takla Makan desert. The wind carried a lethal mushroom cloud over Mongolia and farther to the east, in the direction of Japan.

American U-2 spy planes flew high over China, sucking in by their air intakes samples of radioactive fallout. Higher still, an American spy satellite, following a command sent from thousands of miles away, photographed the event with its powerful cameras.

In the other hemisphere, when most Americans were asleep, telephones rang in the Pentagon and the White House; the message was that a fifth state in the world had just exploded an atomic bomb.

The scientist credited with giving Communist China the bomb is Hsueh-Shen. Dr. Hseuh, who went to China after abandoning his teaching post at the California Institute of Technology, has long been considered to have been a victim of McCarthyism. The London *Times* has learned, however, that in fact an operative of the American Central Intelligence Agency's Department of Plans accompanied Dr. Hseuh to Peking. The American intelligence officer, A. D. Winston, later rose to his present super grade of Deputy Director of Operations . . .

(Please turn to page 3, column 3)

279

EPILOGUE

VIENNA, VIRGINIA—JANUARY 30, 1984
(MONDAY)

"Miss Russell, honey, I want you to try my daddy's remedy . . . Andy's on his way down."

It had snowed until after midnight but now a warm sun had the trees dripping. Molly Kott poured a full jigger of bourbon into the tea mug and put in another wedge of lemon and a full teaspoon of honey.

Molly's robe was too small for Betsy, but it was old and warm and she felt comforted by the touch of the faded corduroy.

"How is your little girl this morning—this afternoon?"

"She's doing fine, thank you. She's still sleeping."

"How far did you get, actually?"

"The Alabama border."

She could hear Andy coming down the stairs. She turned the hot mug slowly to get at the handle. Molly was just about to ask her again if she didn't want something to eat when Andy entered. Both

281

women stared, trying to figure out what it was that seemed different about him.

The dull gray suit was reassuringly rumpled. The fresh blue shirt was faded, the Harvard tie was too narrow, the neatly combed hair was still too short—the familiar look that official Washington knew so well and noticed so little—and now the little man was about to be named the new National Security Adviser to the President.

The stream of sun cut the room in half as he opened the drapes. "Is that her father's Texas recipe?" he asked. He bent stiffly to unplug the telephone. "You look ill," he said to Betsy, "do you want a doctor?"

"Fatigue," she said, "and I can't eat since . . . what is today? When did he—?"

"Wolf's been dead about . . . thirty-eight hours. You passed out here at midnight Sunday, last night, after dictating this." He crossed to a small blond wood chess table. An end game left frozen weeks before toppled apart as he pulled the newspaper across it and handed it to her, then bent stiffly again to retrieve an ivory knight from a dark corner.

"My eyes seem not to want to focus," she said.

"It's the whole front page," he said, sitting down to help her unfold the first section because her hands were still trembling. She read slowly, like a child, moving her lips.

PRESIDENT ACTS
BEIJING SUMMIT RUMORED
Soviet Ambassador Will Meet
New American Security Adviser
in Beijing—Breakthrough Near
for Big Powers
(SPECIAL TO THE WASHINGTON POST FROM THE LONDON
TIMES)
BY
BETSY JONES-RUSSELL

Washington—The London *Times* has learned from an authoritative source that the President of the United States is acting decisively to defuse the big power nuclear confrontation that reached its climax in this capital on Saturday night with the suicide of Wolfgang H. Manheim, the U.S. National Security Adviser.

The *Times* has learned the name of the new American representative chosen by the President to prepare a summit meeting among the three powers involved in the confrontation. Andrew B. Kott, the President's choice, was a close aide of the late Dr. Manheim and, according to intelligence circles, will represent a moderate position vis-à-vis the Soviet Union and the People's Republic of China.

Despite a "worldwide sigh of collective relief"—to quote Senator Edward Kennedy in a major speech in Boston on Sunday —this nation remains extremely tense. Massive antiwar demonstrations scheduled for every major city have been forbidden under the Special Powers Act that went into effect at the height of the crisis on Saturday. Senator Kennedy called former National Security Director Manheim," one of the great Americans in history, a martyr and a patriot," and promised to hold hearings into the late Dr. Manheim's charges against a cabal in the Central Intelligence Agency.

(Please turn to page 3)

He offered to turn the page for her but she let it drop. A telephone rang somewhere. Molly Kott started. "I'll see if she's awake . . ."

Andy folded the paper, then took her hand. She turned her head slowly. She tried to smile. She could see what she must look like registered in his sudden wince.

"Kennedy wants to see you today," he said, "I'm in touch with him, so is the President." More than anyone knows, he thought. "Teddy wants to know what Wolf gave you that you haven't published. He believes that there will be a grace period while I'm in Beijing."

"A grace period?"

"Yes, to expose Winston, Higgins, Kramer—as many of the doomsday people in the Pentagon as we can get."

"Can the President and Kennedy work together? And I thought the President was out of commission—"

"He's functioning now . . . now that he sees the situation in terms of people in his own administration going over the line, he's pulling himself together and, I hope, cleaning house."

"Wick—where is Wick? What happened in California? How did you get back? Your wife . . . what's happening, Andy?"

"Wick is in limbo, being watched . . . I still don't know what happened exactly in California. Someone tried to kill me. Wick was there. Says he was trying to save me. I don't know. It was dark, I was running . . . Then when Wolf went public and I finally talked to Molly . . ."

"You had to come back."

"I had to. After what Wolf did . . . do you want to talk about it? Would it help? I don't know how you—"

Somewhere two telephones started to ring separately. "No calls." His voice carried a resonance of new authority. "What did you say?"

"Power, Andy . . . try not to give in to it . . . use it for however much time you have in Beijing and then, *please,* walk away before . . . well, before it kills you too."

"You think that's what finally drove Wolf to it?"

"In a way . . . power that he had, thought he had. Power that made him victim and instrument . . . and, yes, savior too." She could not possibly describe her role in it, still not sure, still guilty . . .

Upstairs the child began to cry.

"Will you help me with Arbatov? I'm afraid I'm allergic to Russians."

"Well, he's also a Jew, and he's a human being. I guarantee you."

"Yes." He smiled for the first time.

Footsteps crunched on the gravel of the tree-enclosed driveway. Another one of the special marine messengers, she thought.

"I'll have to be going to Camp David in a few minutes," he said.

She nodded slowly, golden hair half covering her ashen face.

"Buchenwald," he said softly. "I think his childhood in the camps must have had something to do with it."

She could hear Molly and the child climbing down the stairs to the game room and the record player start up. Someone had left the tone arm on manual and the volume on loud.

He strained to hear her. ". . . I think a part of all of us died in those camps . . ." He looked behind him. A marine orderly was standing at attention in the hall entrance. "What is it?"

She closed her eyes and let the music wash over her. She heard the orderly's heels click, then Andy Kott's voice from somewhere above her.

"Hu Zuping has been placed under arrest by the Politburo. The members he called 'capitalist roaders' have consolidated their control. They're evacuating the underground cities."

"Thank God . . . poor Mr. Hu . . . So, the Long March is finally over for him."

"Yes . . . well"—he tried to button his suit jacket—"now if Arbatov can get out from under, it would appear that the peacemakers may be back on top—" and he dared to smile for the second time.

She tried too, but silent tears began again.

He reached down to touch her shoulder. "Wolf . . . you and Wolf . . . what he did, but especially what he *said,* it saved us—gave us all another chance. You mustn't give up now."

"No," she whispered, digging for the handkerchief, mugging the smile at last. From below the sounds of a child's record of "The Gingerbread Boy" intruded, making them both smile. "So now the hopes of us all rest on your, ah—"

"Narrow shoulders," he said, "among others. Cowboy boots are too large for me—"

"No," she said, "you're a real American, whatever that is—so was Wolf—and you have something to live for. That has to make a difference."

Someone turned down the volume of the child's song. A car crunched up in front of the house.

"I'm leaving for London, Andy, as soon as I can pull myself together, so I'll say good-bye now."

"I'll be there in the spring, God willing, for the NATO conference."

"God willing," she echoed.

"I believe in God, you know," he said.

"You do? . . . Why?"

"I don't know." Below, the gingerbread boy was still running from the little old man.

"After what almost happened?" she asked. "After Buchenwald? Have you ever visited any of the camps?"

"Poland is full of them," he answered. The driver of the official car in front of the house tapped his horn.

"The world is full of them," she said, dry-eyed at last. "Still waiting."

Behind his polished glasses, Andy Knott's small brown eyes seemed to be looking inward. "In Poland, around the camps, *blawatki* are blooming . . . tiny blue flowers, and *maki,* red poppies—"

"Yes," she said, "*blawatki,* cornflowers, lilac blue, and peonies, and in Czechoslovakia *rapa,* and lilacs at Auschwitz. You can smell them on the breeze."

"Yes," he said, "from miles away."

"Yes," she said, "I see what you mean . . . Now go and say good-bye to your family, Andy. Or, as we used to say, God be with you."